BASEBALL PUZZLES

pil

Publications International, Ltd.

Julie K. Cohen (consultant) is a puzzle developer, puzzle consultant, author, and freelance writer. She has published numerous math puzzle books, and her puzzles for children and adults appear in national magazines, Web sites, puzzle books, cellular phone games, and DVDs. To learn more about Cohen, visit her Web site, http://www.JulieKCohen.com.

Amy Reynaldo (consultant), the author of *How to Conquer* The New York Times *Crossword Puzzle*, created the first crossword blog (*Diary of a Crossword Fiend*) and reviews 1,500 crosswords a year. She is a top-ten finisher at the American Crossword Puzzle Tournament.

Puzzle Constructors: Michael Adams; Cihan Altay; Myles Callum; Jeff Cockrell; Conceptis Puzzles; Holli Fort; Ray Hamel; Luke Haward; Shelly Hazard; Marilynn Huret; Steve Karp; Naomi Lipsky; Dan Meinking; David Millar; Michael Moreci; Alan Olschwang; Ellen F. Pill, Ph.D.; Fred Piscop; Dave Roberts; Marylin Roberts; Stephen Ryder; Paul Seaburn; Fraser Simpson; Terry Stickels; Wayne Robert Williams

Illustrators: Helem An, Jen Torche

Cover Images: Cihan Altay, AP Images, Getty Images, Michael Moreci, Fred Piscop, Wayne Robert Williams

Louis Weber, CEO
Publications International, Ltd.
7373 North Cicero Avenue
Lincolnwood, Illinois 60712

ISBN-13: 978-1-4508-4378-2
ISBN-10: 1-4508-4378-6

Manufactured in USA.

8 7 6 5 4 3 2 1

CONTENTS

BRAIN TRAINING

Yogi Berra famously once said, "Baseball is 90 percent mental. The other half is physical." And like in baseball, where teams hold spring training in Florida and Arizona to get themselves ready for a long season, you need "brain training" to sharpen your mind and protect it from decline. But how do you hone your mental capacity to ensure that you stay on top of your game? Modern-day science provides a clear answer: Protect your mind by exercising your brain. To understand this relationship further, we turn to cutting-edge research.

Protect and Enhance Your Brainpower

Modern-day neuroscience has established that our brain is a far more plastic organ than was previously thought. In the past it was believed that an adult brain could only lose nerve cells (neurons) and couldn't acquire new ones. Today we know that new neurons—and new connections between neurons—continue to develop throughout our lives, even well into advanced age. This process is called *neuroplasticity*. Thanks to recent scientific discoveries, we also know that we can harness the powers of neuroplasticity in protecting and even enhancing our minds at every stage of life—including our advanced years.

How can we harness neuroplasticity to help protect and enhance our mental powers? Recent scientific research demonstrates that the brain responds to mental stimulation much like muscles respond to physical exercise. In other words, you have to give your brain a workout. The more vigorous and diverse your mental life—and the more you welcome mental challenges—the more you will stimulate the growth of new neurons and new connections between them. Furthermore, the *nature* of your mental activities influences *where* in the brain this growth takes place. The brain is a very complex organ with different parts in charge of different mental functions. Thus, different cognitive challenges exercise different components of the brain.

How do we know this? We've learned this by experiments created from real-life circumstances and *neuroimaging*, the high-resolution technologies that allow scientists to study brain structure and function with amazing precision. Some say that these technologies have done for our understanding of the brain what the invention of the telescope has done for our understanding of the planetary systems. Thanks to these technologies, particularly MRI (magnetic resonance imaging), we know that certain parts of the brain exhibit an increased size in those who use these parts of the brain more than most people. For example, researchers have found that the hippocampus, the part of the brain critical for spatial memory, was larger than usual in London cab drivers who have to navigate and remember complex routes in a huge city. Studies revealed that Heschl's gyrus, a part of the temporal lobe of the brain involved in processing music, is larger in professional musicians than in musically untrained people. And the angular gyrus, the part of the brain involved in language, proved to be larger in bilingual individuals than in those who speak only one language.

What is particularly important—the size of the effect, the extent to which the part of the brain was enlarged—was directly related to the *amount of time* each person spent in the activities that rely on the part of the brain in question. For instance, the hippocampal size was directly related to the number of years the cab driver spent on the job, and the size of Heschl's gyrus was associated with the amount of time a musician devoted to practicing a musical instrument. This shows that cognitive activity directly influences the structures of the brain by stimulating the effects of neuroplasticity in these structures, since the enlargement of brain regions implies a greater than usual number of cells or connections between them. The impact of cognitive activity on the brain can be great enough to result in an actual increase in its size! Indeed, different parts of the brain benefit directly from certain activities, and the effect can be quite specific.

Diversify Your Mental Workout

It is also true that any more or less complex cognitive function—be it memory, attention, perception, decision making, or problem solving—relies on a whole network of brain regions rather than on a single region. Therefore, any relatively complex mental challenge will engage more than one part of the brain, yet no single mental activity will engage the entire brain.

This is why the diversity of your mental life is key to your overall brain health. The more vigorous and varied your cognitive challenges, the more efficiently and effectively they'll protect your mind from decline. To return to the workout analogy: Imagine a physical gym. No single exercise machine will make you physically fit. Instead, you need a balanced and diverse workout regimen.

You have probably always assumed that crossword puzzles and sudoku are good for you, and they are. But your cognitive workout will benefit more from a greater variety of exercises, particularly if these exercises have been selected with some knowledge of how the brain works.

The puzzle selection for *Brain Games™: Baseball Puzzles* has been guided by these considerations—with knowledge of the brain and the roles played by its different parts in the overall teamwork of your mental life. We aimed to assemble as wide a range of puzzles as possible in order to offer the brain a full workout.

There is no single magic pill to protect or enhance your mind, but vigorous, regular, and diverse mental activity is the closest thing to it. Research indicates that people who engage in mental activities as a result of their education and vocation are less likely to develop dementia as they age. In fact, many of these people demonstrate impressive mental alertness well into their eighties and nineties.

What's more, the pill does not have to be bitter. You can engage in activities that are both good for your brain *and* fun. Different kinds of puzzles engage different aspects of your mind, and you can assemble them all into a cognitive workout regimen. Variety is the name of the game—that's the whole idea! In any single cognitive workout session, have fun by mixing puzzles of different kinds. This book offers you enough puzzle variety to make this possible.

Welcome challenging puzzles instead of feeling intimidated by them. Never give up! To be effective as a mental workout, the puzzles should not be too easy or too difficult. An overly easy puzzle will not stimulate your brain, just as a leisurely walk in the park is not an efficient way to condition your heart. You need mental exertion. On the other hand, an overly difficult puzzle will just frustrate and discourage you from moving forward. So it is important to find the "challenge zone" that is appropriate for you. This may vary from person to person and from puzzle to puzzle. Here too, the gym analogy applies. Different people will benefit most from different exercise machines and from different levels of resistance and weights.

With this in mind, we have tried to offer a range of difficulty for every puzzle type. Try different puzzles to find the starting level appropriate to you. And before you know it, your puzzle-cracking ability will improve, your confidence will grow, and this will be a source of reassurance, satisfaction, and even pride.

Have Fun While Stretching Your Mind

The important thing is to have fun while doing something good for you. Puzzles can be engaging, absorbing, and even addicting. An increasing number of people make regular physical exercise part of their daily routines and miss it when circumstances prevent them from exercising. These habitual gym-goers know that strenuous effort is something to look forward to, not to avoid. Similarly, you will strengthen your mental muscle by actively challenging it. Don't put the puzzle book down when the solution is not immediately apparent. By testing your mind you will discover the joy of a particular kind of accomplishment: watching your mental powers grow. You must have the feeling of mental effort and exertion in order to exercise your brain.

This brings us to the next issue. While all puzzles are good for you, the degree of their effectiveness as brain conditioners is not the same. Some puzzles only test your knowledge of facts. Such puzzles may be enjoyable and useful to a degree, but they're not as useful in conditioning your brain as the puzzles that require you to transform and manipulate information or do something with it by logic, multistep inference, mental rotation, planning, and so on. The latter puzzles are more likely to give you the feeling of mental exertion, of "stretching your mind," and they are also better for your brain health. You can use this feeling as a useful, though inexact, assessment of a puzzle's effectiveness as a brain conditioner.

Try to select puzzles in a way that complements, rather than duplicates, your job-related activities. If your profession involves dealing with words (e.g., an English teacher), try to emphasize spatial puzzles. If you are an engineer dealing with diagrams, focus on word puzzles. If your job is relatively devoid of mental challenges of any kind, mix several types of puzzles in equal proportions.

Cognitive decline frequently sets in with aging. It often affects certain kinds of memory and certain aspects of attention and decision making. So it is particularly important to introduce cognitive exercise into your lifestyle as you age to counteract any possible cognitive decline. But cognitive exercise is also important for the young and the middle-aged. We live in a world that depends increasingly on the brain more than on brawn. It is important to be sharp in order to get ahead in your career and to remain at the top of your game.

How frequently should you exercise your mind and for how long? Think in terms of an ongoing lifestyle change and not just a short-term commitment. Regularity is key, perhaps a few times a week for 30 to 45 minutes at a time. We've tried to make this easier by offering a whole series of *Brain Games*™ books. You can carry these puzzle books—your "cognitive workout gym"—in your briefcase, backpack, or shopping bag. Our puzzles are intended to be fun, so feel free to fit them into your lifestyle in a way that enhances rather than disrupts it. Research shows that even a relatively brief regimen of vigorous cognitive activity often produces perceptible and lasting effects. But as with physical exercise, the results are best when cognitive exercise becomes a lifelong habit.

Making it fun for the baseball fan is what *Brain Games*™*: Baseball Puzzles* is all about. There are challenges in this book that rely on your knowledge of America's pastime. We've included puzzles that honor greats, such as Babe Ruth, Ted Williams, and Yogi Berra. You may be challenged to unscramble their names or solve a crossword clue about them. Some puzzles may feature a quote from Jackie Robinson or Casey Stengel. There is even a puzzle that commemorates signature home run calls by some of the top baseball broadcasters, such as Vin Scully and Harry Carey.

Now that you're aware of the great mental workout that awaits you in this book, we hope that you'll approach these puzzles with a sense of fun. If you have always been a puzzle fan, we offer a great rationale for indulging your passion! You have not been wasting your time by cracking challenging puzzles—far from it; you have been training and improving your mind.

So, whether you are a new or seasoned puzzle-solver, enjoy your brain workout and get smarter as you go!

GETTING YOUR BRAIN ON DECK

LEVEL 1

Grid Fill

LANGUAGE PLANNING

To complete this puzzle, place the given letters and words into the shapes in this grid. Words and letters will run across, down, and wrap around each shape. When the grid is filled, each row will contain one of the following words: bases, bat, batters, catcher, field, hit, pitcher.

1. F, P, R, T

2. HI, IT, SA, TC

3. CAB, TAB

4. BAIT, HERE

5. CHEST

6. ELDERS

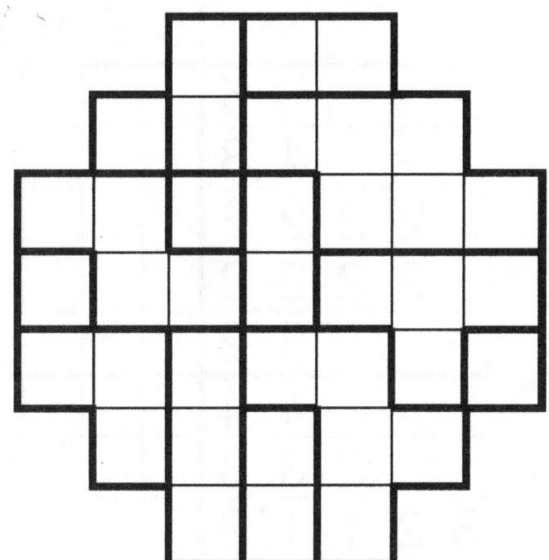

Word Jigsaw

LANGUAGE PLANNING

Fit the pieces into the frame to form common words reading across and down. There's no need to rotate the pieces; they'll fit as shown, with each piece used exactly once. As an added bonus, one of the 9 words will be the last name of a famous baseball player.

AR SW

PY YE

R/O S/O E/N A/D

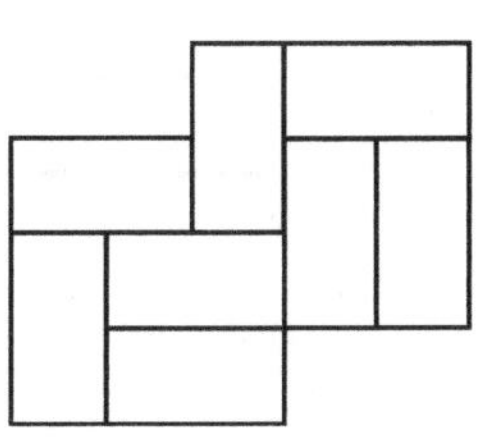

Answers on page 168.

Pic-a-Pix

ANALYSIS LOGIC

Use the clues on the left of every row and the top of every column to reveal the picture hidden in the grid below. Numbers indicate how many blocks get colored in and the sequence in which they get colored. There must be at least one empty block between each sequence. We've filled in some squares to get you started.

	5	6	6	6	12	14	1 3 5	6 1 4	5 3 3	1 1 3	5 3 3	6 1 4	1 2 5	13	11
5															
4 3															
2 2 2 2															
2 2 2 2															
8 2															
4 4															
2 3 3															
3 2 1 1 2															
6 1 1 2															
6 1 1 2															
7 1 1 3															
7 4															
13															
11															
9															

Answer on page 168.

Clubhouse Lingo

ATTENTION | VISUAL SEARCH

Study the illustration below and decipher the 6 bits of baseball terminology.

Word Columns

LANGUAGE | PLANNING

Find the hidden quote from Casey Stengel by using the letters directly below each of the blank squares. Each letter is used only once. A black square indicates the end of a word.

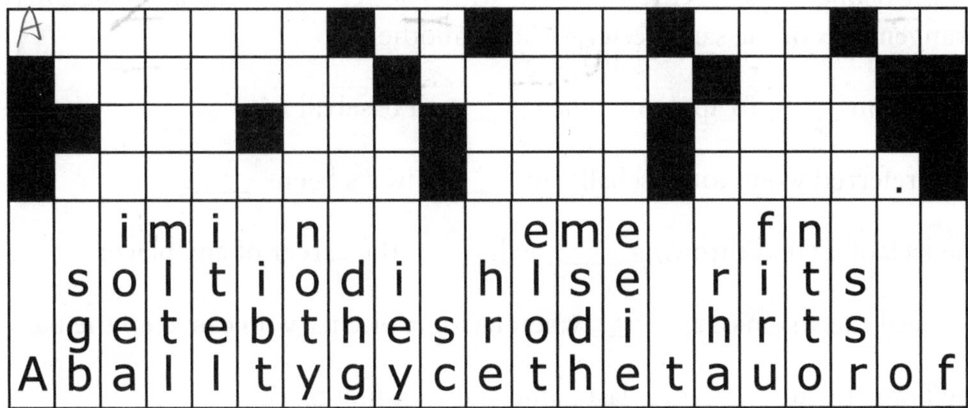

Answers on page 168.

Code-doku

LANGUAGE LOGIC

Solve this puzzle just as you would a sudoku. Use deductive logic to complete the grid so that each row, column, and 3 by 3 box contains each of the letters AEGMORSVY. When you have completed the puzzle, unscramble those 9 letters to reveal the last names of two baseball greats.

<table>
<tr><td>M</td><td></td><td></td><td>Y</td><td>S</td><td>G</td><td></td><td></td><td></td></tr>
<tr><td>G</td><td>S</td><td></td><td></td><td></td><td></td><td></td><td></td><td></td></tr>
<tr><td></td><td></td><td>V</td><td></td><td>A</td><td>M</td><td></td><td></td><td>S</td></tr>
<tr><td></td><td></td><td>Y</td><td></td><td>V</td><td></td><td>E</td><td></td><td>A</td></tr>
<tr><td></td><td>O</td><td></td><td></td><td>M</td><td></td><td></td><td>R</td><td></td></tr>
<tr><td>A</td><td></td><td>G</td><td></td><td>R</td><td></td><td>S</td><td></td><td></td></tr>
<tr><td>Y</td><td></td><td></td><td>A</td><td>O</td><td></td><td>R</td><td></td><td></td></tr>
<tr><td></td><td></td><td></td><td></td><td></td><td></td><td></td><td>V</td><td>O</td></tr>
<tr><td></td><td></td><td></td><td>S</td><td>G</td><td>V</td><td></td><td></td><td>M</td></tr>
</table>

Last names: ______________________________

Play Ball!

LANGUAGE

Fill in the blanks in each sentence below with 3-letter words that are anagrams (rearrangements of the same letters) of one another.

1. There is an _____ to applying pine _____ to a baseball bat.

2. The preferred wood for baseball bats _____ always been _____.

3. The lack of a good throwing _____ will _____ the career of any player.

4. You need the vision of an _____ when facing a pitcher who can keep the ball _____.

5. The home team _____ their last game and is in first place _____.

6. The leadoff batter wants to _____ out of the _____ spot.

Answers on page 168.

42. Actress Skye
43. Strong string
44. Bon _____
45. Treat with a cherry on top
48. Molecule parts
50. Barn dance
52. New York city on the Mohawk
56. Batter-fried morsel
60. Eriq of "E.R."
62. 1993 baseball flick with Thomas Ian Nicholas
64. Choir section
65. Woodworking groove
66. Adams or Falco
67. Baker's need
68. Not difficult
69. Showroom car

DOWN

1. Scotland yard, approximately
2. Ant cow
3. Barely flows
4. Perfume counter bottle
5. Day of the wk.
6. Autograph
7. Batting stat
8. Cattails and such
9. Come clean
10. Indecent
11. Met solo
12. Convenient coffeehouse offering
13. No longer secret
18. Nabokov girl
19. Comedienne Rudner
23. Subscriber's choice
25. Hula hoop, for one
26. Navel buildup?
28. Simple Simon's desire
29. Wax-coated cheese
30. Dynamic beginning
31. Hold up
32. "How sweet _____!"
33. Start of a commandment
34. Chattanooga's home: abbr.
36. Tease
39. Rest stop?
40. _____ Balls (Hostess snack food)
41. Mystify
46. Monet or Picasso, e.g.
47. Extra-wide shoe size
49. Didn't go
51. Wear away
53. _____-France
54. Prospector's filing
55. Correo _____ (Spanish air mail)
56. Ravel out
57. Dramatic part
58. Tiny quantity
59. Ring decisions
60. Old Fords
61. Sailor's call
63. Govt. air-safety outfit

Answers on page 169.

Sequence

ANALYSIS CREATIVE THINKING

Can you complete the sequence below? Hint: Think divisions.

R, A, M, ___

Codeword

ANALYSIS LANGUAGE

The letters of the alphabet are hidden in code: They are represented by a random number from 1 through 26. With the letters already given, complete the crossword puzzle with words and names and break the code. When completed, you'll find the names of 9 players who were on the Chicago White Sox roster in 2009.

1	9	13	6	24	1	9			20	6	24	19
26		9		6		23		8		13		2
13	26	25		16	6	13	1	10		22	3	6
5		26		6				1		9		7
10	13	9	23	17	8	4		10	6	23	6	24
		2		18		24						11
8	19	10		10	1	26	6	24		19	6	6
15						14		8		6		
2	13	24	26	5		4	2	14	26	17	6	22
26		8		8				26		1		8
21	8	18		21	6	23	6	24		7	6	13
6		26		21		9		6		8		1
24	26	9	10			6	13	12	3	14	6	10

1	2	3	4	5	6 E	7	8	9	10	11	12	13
14	15	16	17	18	19 B	20 V	21	22	23	24 R	25	26

Answers on pages 169–170.

Word Columns

LANGUAGE PLANNING

Find the hidden quote from Casey Stengel by using the letters directly below each of the blank squares. Each letter is used only once. A black square indicates the end of a word unless the word ends at the end of a row.

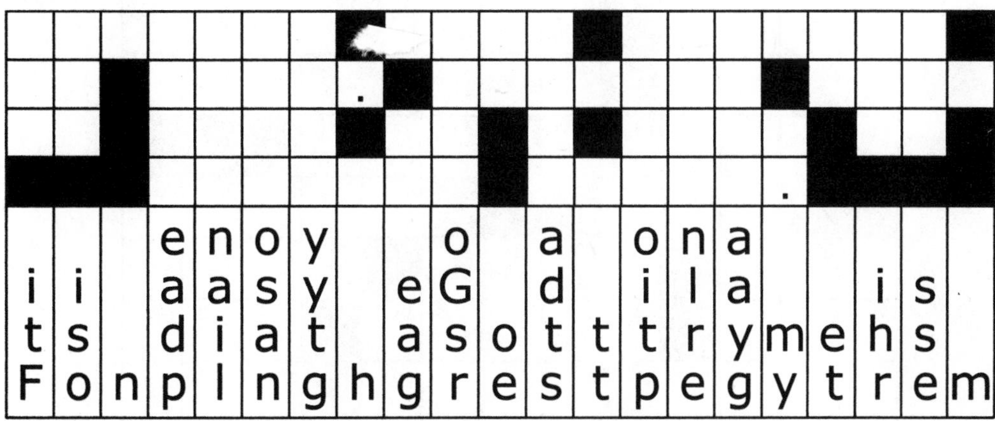

Baseball Superstitions

LANGUAGE LOGIC

Cryptograms are messages in substitution code. Break the code to read an interesting baseball fact. For example, THE SMART CAT might become FVO QWGDF JGF if **F** is substituted for **T, V** for **H, O** for **E,** and so on.

YNY VPZ WDPT SUFS SV BPGG GOPZJUS F

GQFBW GFS SP KMKOV JFHK YZONDJ SUK

1907 AKFAPD, GZS DKMKO ZAKY NS PDBK?

Answers on page 171.

Getting Your Brain On Deck

Play Ball!

GENERAL KNOWLEDGE | LANGUAGE

1	2	3	4	■	5	6	7	■	8	9	10	11
12				■	13			■	14			
15				■	16			17				
18				19		■	20			■	■	■
■	■	21			■	■	■	22		23	24	25
26	27		■	28	29	30	31	■	32			
33			■	34				35	■	36		
37			38	■	39				■	40		
41				42	■	■	■	43	44		■	■
■	■	■	45		46	■	47				48	49
50	51	52				53		■	54			
55				■	56			■	57			
58				■	59			■	60			

ACROSS

1. ____ Ruth, "The Sultan of Swat"
5. Once around the track
8. _____ out (is retired on an easy fly)
12. "I smell _____!" (words from the suspicious)
13. Quarterback Manning
14. Kind of sax
15. Accompanied by
16. Time for a class picnic, perhaps
18. Regret greatly
20. Many a Little League coach
21. Bullring cry
22. Bus station
26. Flow back, like the tide
28. Stand in line, e.g.

32. In _____ straits
33. Hawaiian floral wreath
34. Homeless cat or dog
36. Ball supporter for young Little Leaguers
37. Disappear, like snow
39. "A _____ coincidence"
40. Grifter
41. Howard of satellite radio
43. Baseball bat wood
45. Corn serving
47. Squares, circles, etc.
50. Small motorboat
54. Like sports telecasts, often
55. Randy Johnson, "The Big _____"
56. Cool _____ cucumber
57. Very top
58. _____ up (does a relief stint in a blowout game)
59. Tampa Bay player
60. Declare untrue

DOWN

1. Cry like a baby
2. Operatic solo
3. Auto seen around Gotham City
4. "I Love Lucy" neighbor _____ Mertz
5. _____ on base (inning stat)
6. Boxing great Muhammad _____
7. The _____ Piper
8. Like an umpire's chest protector
9. Casey Stengel, "The _____ Professor"
10. School org.
11. _____ sauce (Chinese restaurant condiment)
17. Young fellow
19. Anchorman's broadcast
23. Device used to tune an instrument
24. Nabisco cookie since 1912
25. Typical MTV viewer
26. Shade trees
27. Red veggie
29. $20s dispenser
30. Ill temper
31. _____ and feather (old punishment)
35. Slangy assent
38. Rewards for doggie tricks
42. Throw out on an attempted steal, say
44. Fare for dieters
46. Crowd sound
47. Hang around
48. All tied up
49. Alluring, like a supermodel
50. Pirate's quaff
51. Card game with Skip and Reverse cards
52. Beat, but barely
53. World Baseball Classic team

Answers on page 171.

Baseball Tamagram

ANALYSIS LOGIC

Find an expression to define the illustration below, and then rearrange the letters of it to form a 10-letter phrase (3 letters and 7 letters) that defines the top-of-the-rotation pitcher. LLL, for example, is THREE L'S, which is a rearrangement of SHELTER.

Trivia on the Brain

All of these players have hit 4 home runs in a single game: Bobby Lowe, Ed Delahanty, Lou Gehrig, Chuck Klein, Pat Seerey, Gil Hodges, Joe Adcock, Rocky Colavito, Willie Mays, Mike Schmidt, Bob Horner, Mark Whiten, Mike Cameron, Shawn Green, and Carlos Delgado.

Answer on page 171.

Elevator Words

GENERAL KNOWLEDGE | LANGUAGE

Like an elevator, words move up and down the "floors" of this puzzle. Starting with the first answer, the second part of each answer carries down to become the first part of the following answer. With the clues given, complete the puzzle.

	Clues
1. Ball _____	1. A free pass to first base
2. _____ _____	2. Eighty years, in Lincoln's day
3. __________	3. Where in-game stats are found
4. _____ _____	4. Monopoly, for example
5. _____ _____	5. Sports page wrap-up
6. _____ Reel	6. Video of outstanding plays

Grid Fill

LANGUAGE | PLANNING

To complete this puzzle, place the given letters and words into the shapes in this grid. Words and letters will run across, down, and wrap around each shape. When the grid is filled, each row will contain one of the following words or phrases: fouls, hit, home run, run, strikes, umpires, walks.

1. I, K, L, W

2. AH, ER, ES, FO, RE, SS, UL, UN

3. KIT, ROM, SUN, TRI

4. HUMPS

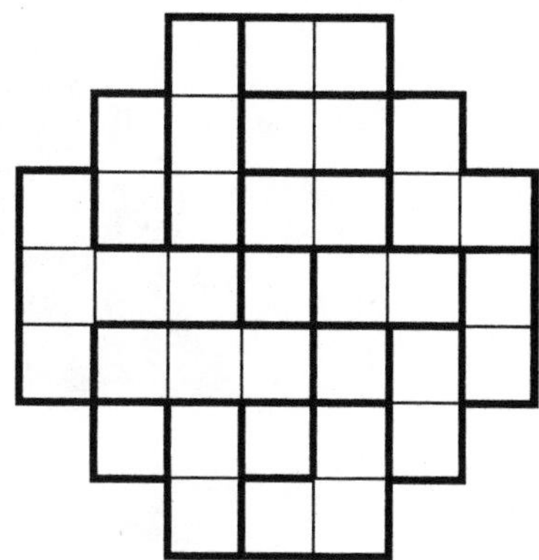

Answers on page 171.

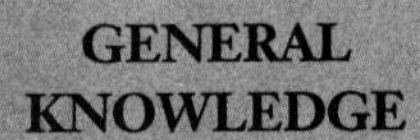

Mix n' Match

Match the baseball movie to its featured team.

Angels in the Outfield	☐	☐	Hackensack Bulls
Bad News Bears	☐	☐	Rockford Peaches
Brewster's Millions	☐	☐	California Angels
Bull Durham	☐	☐	New York Knights
Damn Yankees	☐	☐	Durham Bulls
Eight Men Out	☐	☐	Washington Senators
Field of Dreams	☐	☐	Chico's Bail Bond Bears
A League of Their Own	☐	☐	Cleveland Indians
Major League	☐	☐	Chicago White Sox
The Natural	☐	☐	Chicago White Sox

Answers on page 171.

Team Search

ATTENTION | VISU[illegible] SEARCH

Every team listed is contained within the group of letters. Words can b[illegible]ound in a straight line horizontally, vertically, or diagonally. They may be read e[illegible]her forward or backward. Leftover letters spell a quote from Yankee legend Mickey [illegible]antle.

Bonus: What MLB team is missing from this list?

ANGELS	MARLINS	ROYALS	WHITE SOX
ASTROS	METS	TIGERS	YANKEES
ATHLETICS	NATIONALS	TWINS	
BLUE JAYS	ORIOLES		
BRAVES	PADRES		
BREWERS	PHILLIES		
CARDINALS	PIRATES		
CUBS	RANGERS		
DODGERS	RAYS		
GIANTS	REDS		
INDIANS	RED SOX		
MARINERS	ROCKIES		

A T E A [illegible] S S I S S W H E B R
E S A B [illegible] T [illegible] C R A N G E R S
O E S [illegible] R N S E I K C O R E N
C E A [illegible] I A G [illegible] N T N P R W A
O K Y L E I V A A E E H I E I
S N [illegible] C T G T E D J U L P R D
R [illegible] S A S I D S [illegible] T E M H S N
M [illegible] E A O L G O N E O U I T I
N [illegible] T N H C A R D [illegible] N A L S A
[illegible] E A G A S O Y W N W S L B A
[illegible] L R E D S O X O S [illegible] T I H W
S O I L A N T M A R [illegible] [illegible] E R S
G I P S I S W R D A E [illegible] S E B
R R E A C O W A O Y A [illegible] [illegible] D U
G O O E S T P O H S I D [illegible] E C

Leftover letters: ______________________________

____

Answers on page 172.

Grid Fill

LANGUAGE PLANNING

To complete this puzzle, place the given letters and words into the shapes in this grid. Words and letters will run across, down, and wrap around each shape. When the grid is filled, each row will contain one of the following words: bat, batters, fly, glove, infield, peanuts, pitch.

1. B, B, G, I, S

2. CH, FL, LD, LY, PA

3. EVE, FIT, OAT, PIN, TEA, TEN

4. RUTS

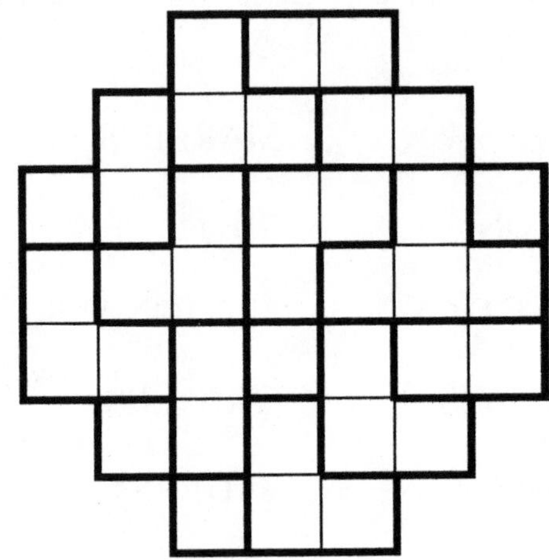

Take Me Out to the Ball Game

ANALYSIS COMPUTATION

For millions of fans, baseball means the Yankees. Can you prove it true by substituting the letters below into numbers? Hint: Zero cannot begin a word. For this puzzle, A=6, E=8, K=5, and S=4.

```
   BASE
   BALL
+ GAMES
-------
  YANKS
```

Answers on page 172.

Word Columns

LANGUAGE PLANNING

Find the hidden quote about a famous player by using the letters directly below each of the blank squares. Each letter is used only once. A black square indicates the end of a word.

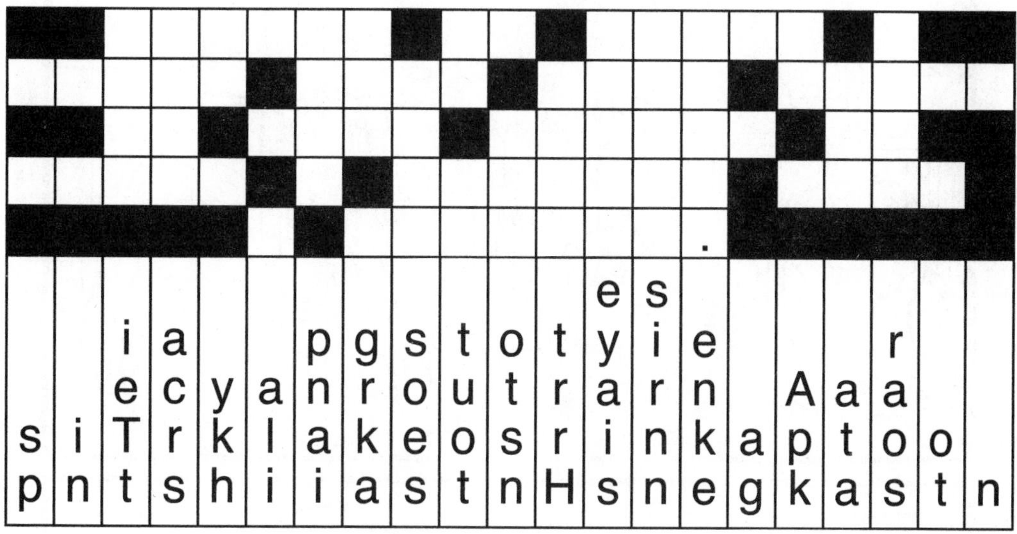

Hall of Fame Nicknames

LANGUAGE

If you know your baseball Hall of Famers and their nicknames, you won't have much trouble figuring out these anagrammed names.

1. BOW SAGGED, aka "Chicken Man" ______________

2. HER BALLCLUB, aka "The Meal Ticket" ______________

3. NEGLECT ESSAY, aka "The Old Perfessor" ______________

4. DUNK DESIRE, aka "The Silver Fox" ______________

Answers on page 172.

The Right Stuff

ATTENTION VISUAL SEARCH

Can you spot the 10 differences between these dugout scenes?

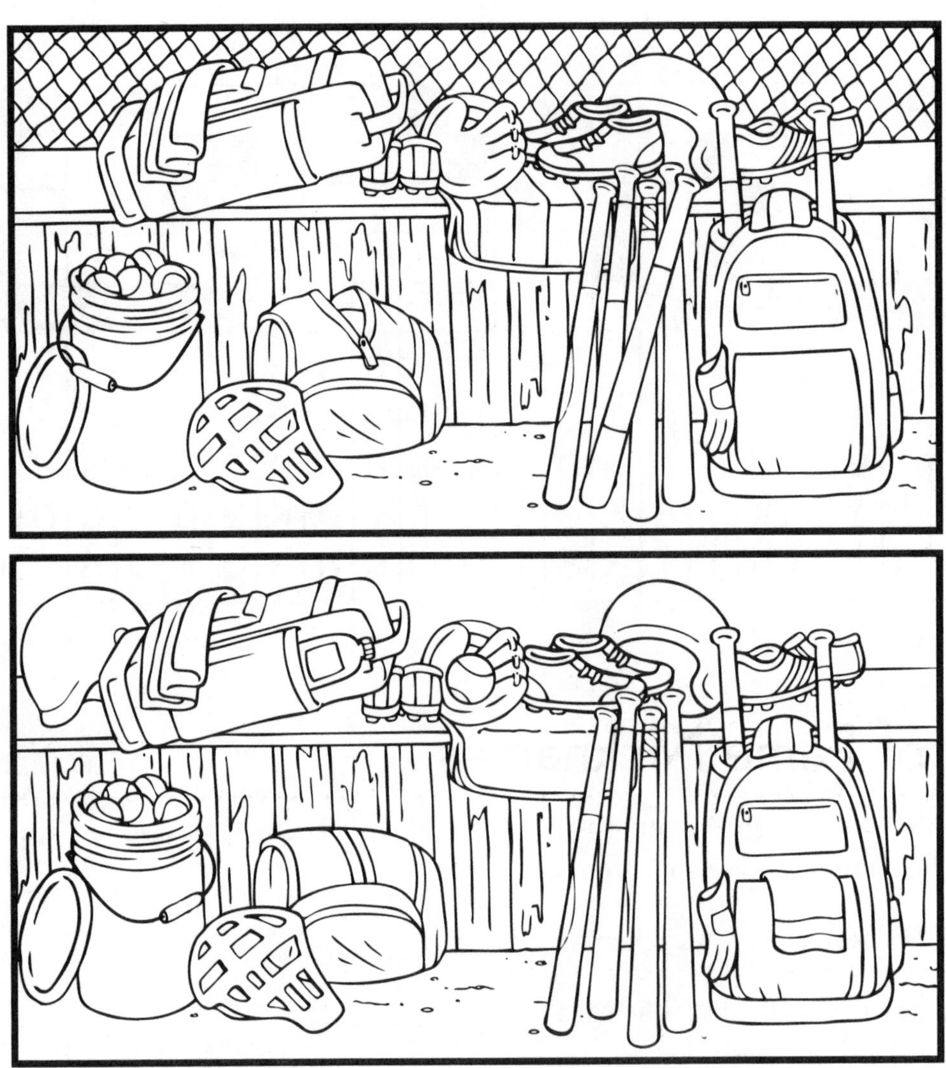

Answers on page 172.

Name Calling

ANALYSIS

Decipher the encoded words in the quote from Humphrey Bogart below using the numbers and letters on the phone pad. Remember that each number can stand for 3 or 4 possible letters.

"A hot dog at the 2–2–5–5–4–2–6–3 beats 7–6–2–7–8 2–3–3–3 at the Ritz."

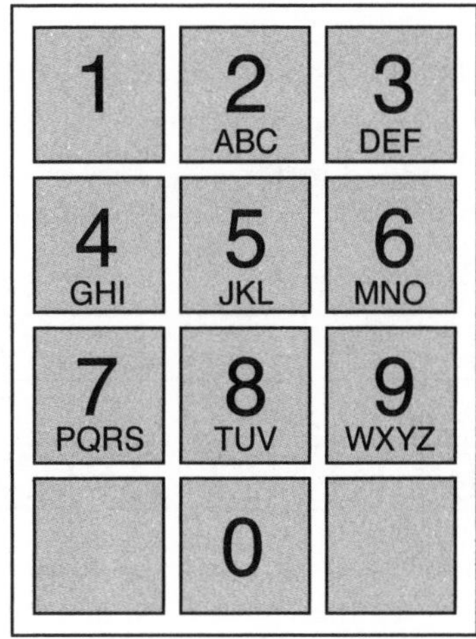

Shifter

ANALYSIS LOGIC

Solve the word for either clue, then shift each letter to its new spot, following the lines from one box to another.

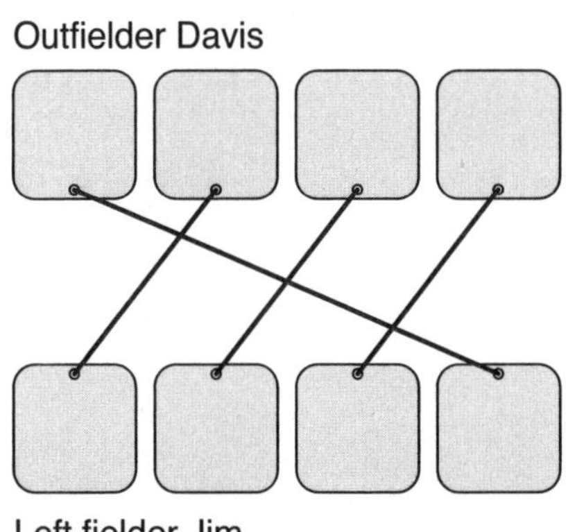

Answers on page 173.

Baseball Terminology Letterbox

LOGIC PLANNING

The letters in BASES can be found in boxes 4, 6, 20, and 25, but not necessarily in that order. Similarly, the letters in all the other baseball terms can be found in the boxes indicated. Your task is to insert all the letters of the alphabet into the boxes. If you do this correctly, the shaded cells will reveal another baseball term.

Hint: Look for words that share a single letter. For example, BASES shares a **B** with BULLPEN and an **A** with MAJORS. By comparing the number lists, you can then deduce the box numbers of the shared letters.

1	2	3	4	5	6	7	8	9	10	11	12	13
14	**15**	**16**	**17**	**18**	**19**	**20**	**21**	**22**	**23**	**24**	**25**	**26**
												Q

BASEBALL: 4, 12, 16, 20, 25

BASES: 4, 16, 20, 25

BOX SCORE: 2, 4, 5, 9, 16, 18, 20

BULLPEN: 4, 6, 7, 12, 19, 20

FLY BALL: 11, 12, 17, 20, 25

FOUL OUT: 2, 6, 12, 17, 24

MAJORS: 2, 3, 5, 10, 16, 25

PITCHER: 1, 4, 5, 18, 19, 23, 24

POP FLY: 2, 11, 12, 17, 19

RELIEVER: 4, 5, 12, 13, 23

SAVED GAME: 3, 4, 13, 16, 21, 22, 25

STRIKE ZONE: 2, 4, 5, 7, 8, 14, 16, 23, 24

WALK: 12, 14, 15, 25

WINDUP: 6, 7, 15, 19, 21, 23

Answer on page 173.

Going . . . Going . . . Gone!

CREATIVE THINKING | LANGUAGE

Arrange the following words in the blanks below to reveal home run calls by famous announcers.

back; back; back; Bye; bye; coming back; could be; cow; flight; forget; going; Good-bye; goodbye; grand salami; Holy; is; Kiss; might be; mustard; rye bread; show movies

1. " _____ _____ baby!" —Russ Hodges
2. " _____ it!" —Vin Scully
3. "Get out the _____ _____ and _______ grandma, cause it's ____ _____ time!" —Dave Neihaus
4. "_____ baseball!" —Dick Risenhoover
5. "_____ _____!" —Phil Rizzuto
6. "It ____ ____, it _____ _____. . . it _____! A home run!" —Harry Caray
7. "_____ it _____!" —Bob Prince
8. "That ball is _____ and it ain't ________ ________!" —Jeff Kingery
9. "They usually _______ _______ on a _____ like that." —Ken Coleman
10. "Back, _____, _____, _____. . . Gone!" —Chris Berman

Trivia on the Brain

The field used in the 1989 movie *Field of Dreams* took only 3 days to construct. It still exists, and the owners charge no admission for tourists to come and play ball there.

Answers on page 173.

Close Call

ATTENTION VISUAL SEARCH

Can you find 8 things wrong with this exciting play at the plate?

Answers on page 173.

Lineup Card

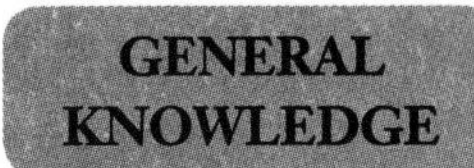

Fill in the blanks to spell out the names of great players and managers associated with a particular team. Every occurrence of every letter of that team's name has been filled in. As a bonus, can you name the team?

1. ___ ___ o D ___ r o ___ ___ ___ ___
2. ___ e e ___ e e R e e s e
3. D ___ ___ e S ___ ___ d e r
4. ___ ___ ___ ___ ___ e R o ___ ___ ___ s o ___
5. D o ___ D r ___ s d ___ ___ e
6. S ___ ___ ___ ___ ___ o ___ ___ ___ ___
7. ___ o ___ ___ ___ ___ ___ s o r d ___
8. D o ___ S ___ ___ ___ o ___
9. G ___ ___ ___ o d g e s
10. S ___ e ___ e G ___ r ___ e ___

Team: ______________

Answers on page 173.

Fitting Words

GENERAL KNOWLEDGE | PLANNING

In this miniature crossword, the clues are listed randomly and are numbered for convenience only. It is up to you to figure out the placement of the 9 answers. To help you, we've inserted one letter in the grid, and this is the only occurrence of that letter in the completed puzzle.

1. He hit 61 in '61
2. Demonic
3. Big throw
4. Blue Jays or White Sox
5. Take five
6. Silvery fish
7. Resistance units
8. Tortoise racer
9. None of the above

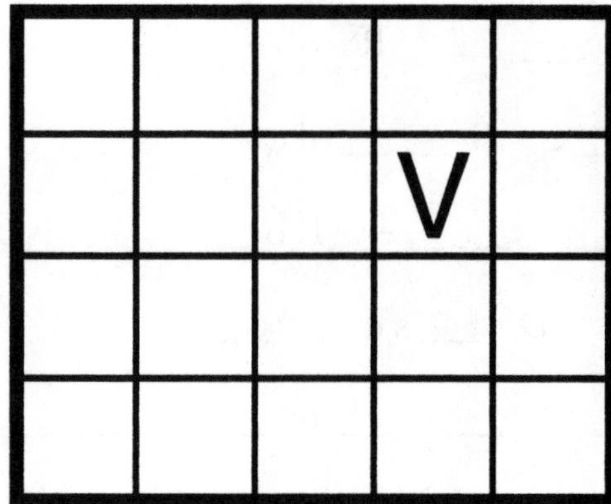

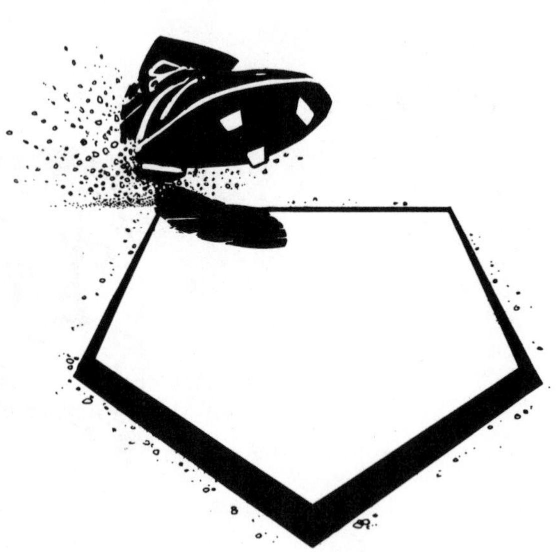

Answer on page 173.

Yer Out!

PLANNING SPATIAL REASONING

Can you guide the path of the ball to the fielder's mitt?

Answer on page 173.

Full Count

ANALYSIS LOGIC

How many times can you find the word BASEBALL in the grid by proceeding from letter to consecutive letter while moving between edge-to-edge or corner-to-corner neighboring cells?

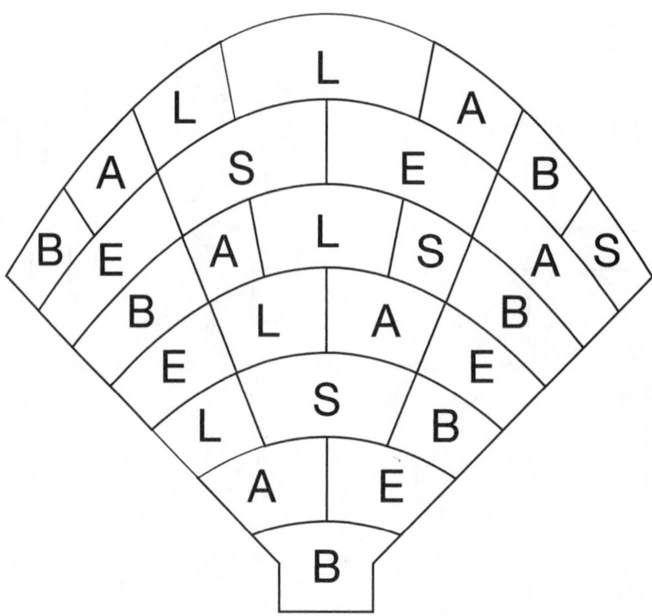

Trivia on the Brain

A baseball lasts only about 8 days in the majors. It gets used once in a game before being demoted for use in batting practice. After it's been hit once or twice, it goes to the batting cages under the stands for a 4- or 5-day beating—then it leaves the park for good.

Answer on page 173.

Codeword

ANALYSIS LANGUAGE

The letters of the alphabet are hidden in code: They are represented by a random number from 1 through 26. With the letters already given, complete the crossword puzzle with words and names and break the code. When completed, you'll find the names of 9 players who were on the Tampa Bay Rays roster in 2009.

4	25	22	18	13	10	1	■	■	17	7	12	21
■	4	■	19	■	13	■	21	■	19	■	25	■
15	25	5	17	25	18	13	19	■	18	19	18	8
■	5	■	■	■	8	■	4	■	4	■	23	■
10	8	2	7	13	5	■	23	8	19	5	13	8
■	■	■	18	■	■	■	13	■	■	■	8	■
22	25	7	5	12	8	■	18	25	10	19	18	6
■	26	■	■	■	5	■	■	■	8	■	■	■
18	8	17	8	5	1	■	14	25	3	8	15	15
■	18	■	16	■	13	■	8	■	■	■	7	■
24	8	5	19	■	12	18	19	3	20	25	18	9
■	19	■	12	■	8	■	1	■	25		8	■
10	1	8	1	■	■	10	14	13	8	15	9	10

1 T	2	3	4	5	6	7	8 E	9	10	11 J	12	13
14 H	15	16	17	18	19	20	21	22	23	24	25	26

Answer on page 173.

Chalk Talk

ANALYSIS LANGUAGE

Can you "read" the 6 baseball phrases on the chalkboard?

How Much?

ANALYSIS PROBLEM SOLVING

Four veteran players (LeBucks, Peydey, Jacques, and Lefty) from the local baseball team were at their favorite sports bar discussing how much they had signed for in their rookie years. The bartender was hoping to become a sports agent someday, so he offered to guess the rookie year salaries of each. The veterans wrote their rookie year salaries on a piece of paper: \$8 million, \$14 million, \$12 million, and \$10 million. The shortstop said he signed for the most money. LeBucks signed for more than Peydey, and the pitcher signed for more than Jacques, the catcher. Lefty refused to give a hint. Peydey, the first baseman, did not sign for \$10 million, and neither did Jacques. Using this information, can you help the bartender figure out the position for each player and what their rookie year salaries were?

Answers on page 173.

Rhyme Time

GENERAL KNOWLEDGE | LANGUAGE

Each clue leads to a 2-word answer that rhymes, such as BIG PIG or STABLE TABLE. The numbers in parentheses after the clue give the number of letters in each word of the answer. For example, "cookware taken from the oven (3, 3)" would be "hot pot."

1. A skinny Minnesotan (4, 4): ______________
2. A more en-vogue manager (6, 7): ________________
3. A cynical batsman (6, 6): ________________
4. Ripken's friends (4, 4): ________________
5. A beefy official (5, 3): ________________
6. Given to throwing strikes (4, 5): ________________
7. The opposite of a fastball (4, 5): ________________
8. A ball that soars skyward off the bat (4, 3): ________________
9. A more-recent Milwaukee arrival (5, 6): ________________
10. DiMaggio's dingers (4, 5): ________________

Answers on page 174.

Pic-a-Pix

ANALYSIS LOGIC

Use the clues on the left of every row and the top of every column to reveal a hitter's profile hidden in the grid below. Numbers indicate how many blocks get colored in, and the sequence in which they get colored. There must be at least one empty block between each sequence.

	1	6 2	12	10 2	6 1 1 2	8 1 2	6 1 4	5 3 3	4 1 3	4 2 2 1 1	4 1 1	3 2 3	1 1 2	2	1
8															
10															
10															
12															
7 1															
6 7															
3 1 1 1 1															
5 1 1															
3 1 2															
5 1 1															
2 1 1															
4 1 1															
8															
5															
4															

Answer on page 174.

Word Jigsaw

LANGUAGE PLANNING

Fit the pieces into the frame to form common words reading across and down. There's no need to rotate the pieces; they'll fit as shown, with each piece used exactly once. Hint: One of the 9 words will be the last name of a famous Yankee shortstop and captain.

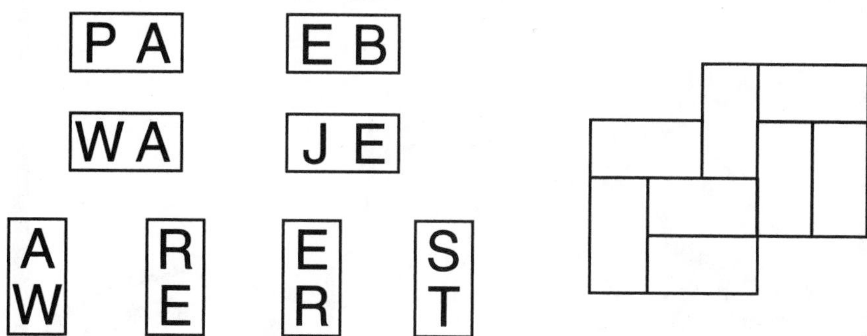

Word Ladder

LANGUAGE PLANNING

Use the clues to change just one letter on each line to go from the top word to the bottom word. Do not change the order of the letters. You must have a common English word at each step.

BATTER

________ witty exchange

________ to haggle

________ holds up your stocking

________ to gather

________ person who makes silly faces

BURNER

Answers on page 174.

Picture This

ATTENTION VISUAL SEARCH

Can you figure out the names of 5 baseball greats by identifying the visual representations of their nicknames in the illustration below?

Answers on page 174.

Level 2

Rhyme Time

GENERAL KNOWLEDGE | LANGUAGE

Each clue leads to a 2-word answer that rhymes, such as BIG PIG or STABLE TABLE. The numbers in parentheses after the clue give the number of letters in each word of the answer. For example, "cookware taken from the oven (3, 3)" would be "hot pot."

1. A Bronx Bomber's tissue (6, 5): ______________

2. What Maddux's feet are attached to (5, 4): ________________

3. The first-year player's Oreos (7, 7): ________________

4. The Green Monster (4, 4): ________________

5. Shake off the catcher's sign (6, 5): ________________

6. The stadium at night, once the lights are out (4, 4): ________________

7. A heavier hitter (6, 6): ________________

8. Frighten Dodger legend Snider (5, 4): ________________

Trivia on the Brain

In a 1951 game between the Braves and the Dodgers, the umpire not only ejected the players who kept arguing with him but also the entire Dodgers bench—which included Bill Sharman. That made him the only player to have been ejected from a major league baseball game without ever having played in the majors. Sharman's real game was basketball, however. He was enshrined in the Basketball Hall of Fame in 1976 as a player and in 2004 as a coach.

Answers on page 174.

Swing Batter!

PLANNING

SPATIAL REASONING

Can you follow the ball as it curves its way toward the batter's swing?

Answer on page 174.

Baseball Able Labs

LANGUAGE

Fill in the blanks in each sentence below with 4-letter words that are anagrams (rearrangements of the same letters) of one another.

1. To be a good _____ leader a player must _____ his own ego.

2. Ballpark venders' slogan: Everyone _____ without leaving their _____.

3. The shortstop _____ a twinge in his back every time he moved to his _____.

4. The frugal team owner bought a _____ that only covers _____ of the infield.

5. The batter was able to _____ around the bases after the ball passed just inside of the foul _____.

6. _____ of teams have _____ both games of a doubleheader.

Word Ladder

LANGUAGE PLANNING

Using the clues along the way, change just one letter on each line to go from the top word to the bottom word. Do not change the order of the letters. You must have a common English word at each step.

BALL

____

_______ opposite of succeed

____

_______ baseball's out of bounds

FOUR

Answers on page 174.

Say It Ain't So!

ATTENTION VISUAL SEARCH

All the words and names below are related to the 1919 Black Sox scandal. They can be found in the grid in a straight line horizontally, vertically, or diagonally. They may be read either forward or backward. Leftover letters spell a fact about the scandal.

R O S C A R F E L S C H
E A L L T H R O U G O Y
V H B A N N E D G H N E
A E R U E F D A A U S K
E S E D D T M O M J P S
W O I E N B C I E N I I
K T H W L E M F F I R M
C X T I H I U R I D A O
U B N L C A L S X E C C
B G I L M H L A N B Y S
E D D I E C I C O T T E
N F U A C K N C W E A L
A U L V M F F O Y A P E R
G M R W A S R O R R E G A A
D B S B A N D N E D W I T O H
L L H T H E O G N I T T E B T C
S H O E L E S S J O E J A C K S O N H
E R N S S F O R N O T B L A C K S O X R
G R E B S I R S E L R A H C E S P O R
A T I N G I T S E I R E S D L R O W

ARNOLD ("Chick") GANDIL

BANNED

BETTING

BLACK SOX

BUCK WEAVER

CHARLES COMISKEY

CHARLES ("Swede") RISBERG

CHICAGO

CLAUDE ("Lefty") WILLIAMS

CONSPIRACY

EDDIE CICOTTE

ERRORS

FRED MCMULLIN

FUMBLES

GAMBLING

GAME FIX

OSCAR ("Happy") FELSCH

PAYOFF

SCANDAL

SHOELESS JOE JACKSON

WORLD SERIES

Leftover letters: ______________________________

Answers on page 174.

He's the Man(ager)

LANGUAGE LOGIC

Cryptograms are messages in substitution code. Break the code to read an interesting baseball stat. For example, THE SMART CAT might become FVO QWGDF JGF if **F** is substituted for **T, V** for **H, O** for **E,** and so on.

TZDFCOKFTZDC C'Q (JSI EZK SCVFCJO

CEZFKEDLQ) RCJCWKA LSJJDK RCLV ZCQ 3,731

LCAKKA NDLESADKQ, RSAK EZCJ CJU SEZKA

RCJCWKA DJ ZDQESAU.

Shifter

ANALYSIS LOGIC

Solve the word for either clue, then shift each letter to its new spot, following the lines from one box to another.

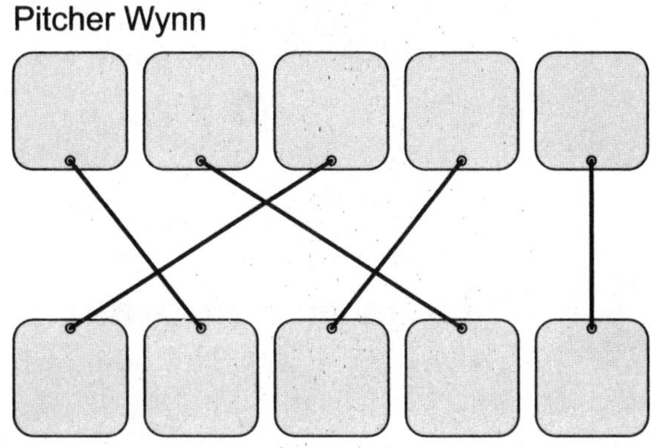

Answers on pages 174–175.

Curveball

ANALYSIS LOGIC

Starting from each number outside the grid, draw a line leading from that number to a mitt. No lines can intersect, and the number of boxes the line must pass through coincides with the number it originates from. So, if a line starts at the number 6, it must pass through 6 boxes (including the box the mitt is in). All boxes will be used.

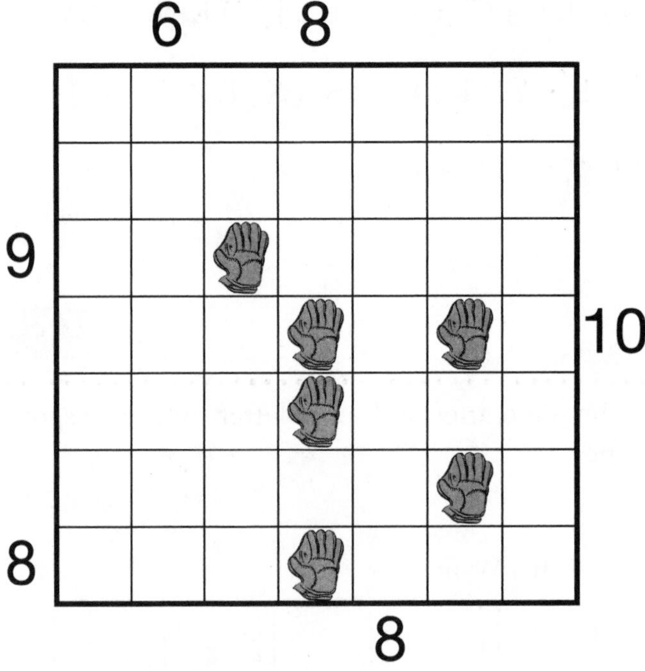

Trivia on the Brain

Prior to 1931, if a fly ball bounced over or through the outfield fence it was considered a home run!

Answer on page 175.

Network

ANALYSIS LOGIC

Place letters into the empty circles so that the given phrase can be spelled out in order from letter to consecutive letter through connected circles. Letters can be used more than once, and you can double-back to use a previously used letter.

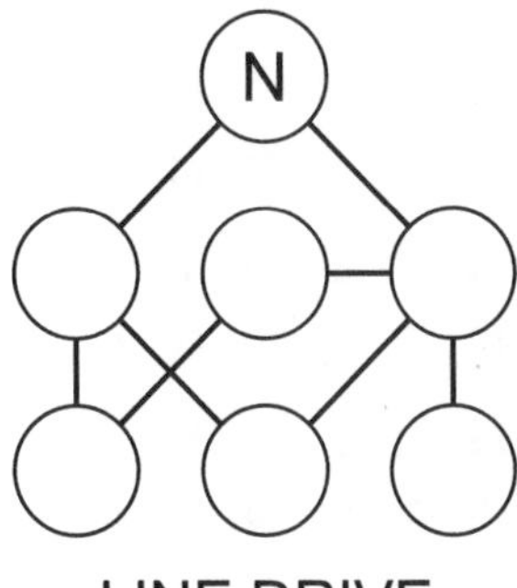

LINE DRIVE

Word Ladder

LANGUAGE PLANNING

Using the clues along the way, change just one letter on each line to go from the top word to the bottom word. Do not change the order of the letters. You must have a common English word at each step.

DRAG

________ boast

____

____

________ crooked

BUNT

Answers on page 175.

Pitcher Perfect

ATTENTION VISUAL SEARCH

As of 2010, only 20 major-league pitchers have tossed a perfect game. Every name listed below is contained within the group of letters on the next page. Names can be found in a straight line horizontally, vertically, or diagonally. They may read either forward or backward.

K H N R E K R A B N E L D A R T J
B V O E E N O C D I V A D D Y O H
R A S D D T I X A N V N D E H M P
O E T D D R N O M I O A R N T B I
Y N R O S E Z U D M P I W N T R N
H C E N H R E W H D N A I I N O O
A G B L E P E C E H R R F S E W S
L N O A C L I G T D S I N M N N N
L I R R L R I N O G S I O A N I H
A N E S E L Y T O R Y I F R E N O
D N I E L G N U O Y Y C D T A G J
A U L N B A S E I N E N X I A T Y
Y B R S S O J E I D D A N N R C D
O M A R K B U E H R L E A E I N N
Z I H T T I W E K I M N I Z K N A
C J C G S A N D Y K O U F A X S R
Q P A L N E D A R B S A L L A D P

LEN BARKER

DALLAS BRADEN

TOM BROWNING

MARK BUEHRLE

JIM BUNNING

DAVID CONE

ROY HALLADAY

CATFISH HUNTER

RANDY JOHNSON

ADDIE JOSS

SANDY KOUFAX

DON LARSEN

DENNIS MARTINEZ

LEE RICHMOND

CHARLIE ROBERTSON

KENNY ROGERS

JOHN WARD

DAVID WELLS

MIKE WITT

CY YOUNG

Answers on page 175.

Grid Fill

LANGUAGE PLANNING

To complete this puzzle, place the given letters and words into the shapes in this grid. Words and letters will run across, down, and wrap around each shape. When the grid is filled, each row will contain one of the following words: batters, fan, field, infield, out, strikes, teams.

1. B, O, S, T
2. AN, FI, FI, MS, SD
3. EAU, FAT, TRI
4. KEEL
5. ELDER, STINT

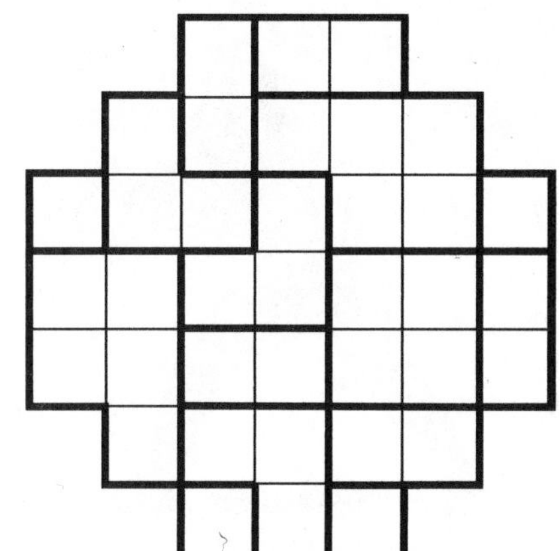

Word Jigsaw

LANGUAGE PLANNING

Fit the pieces into the frame to form common words reading across and down. There's no need to rotate the pieces; they'll fit as shown, with each piece used exactly once. As an added bonus, one of the 9 words will be the last name of a famous Yankee player and noted rhetorician.

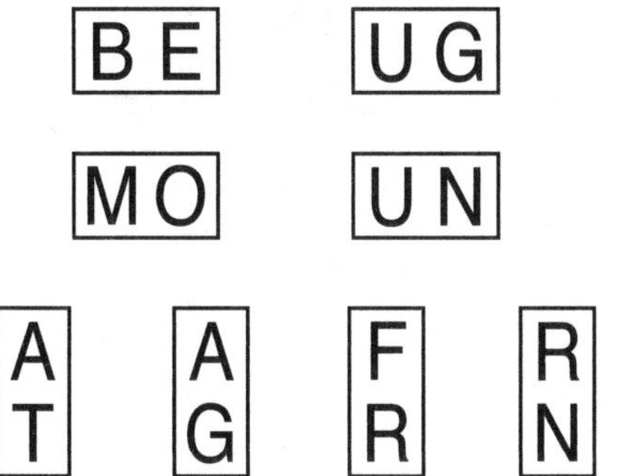

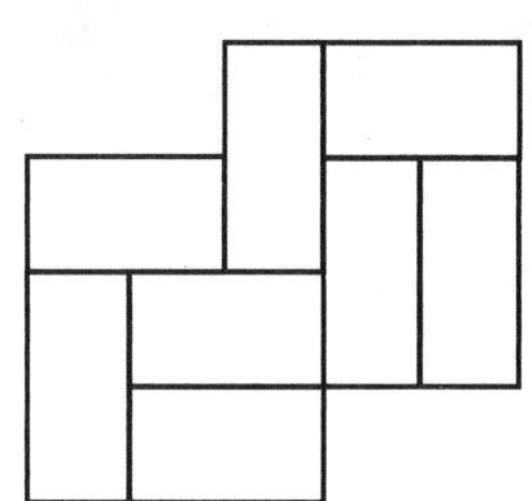

Answers on page 175.

Batter Up!

ATTENTION VISUAL SEARCH

Which silhouette matches the batter in the middle exactly?

Answer on page 175.

Level 2

Rhyme Time

GENERAL KNOWLEDGE | LANGUAGE

Each clue leads to a 2- or 3-word answer that rhymes, such as BIG PIG or STABLE TABLE. The numbers in parentheses after the clue give the number of letters in each word of the answer. For example, "cookware taken from the oven (3, 3)" would be "hot pot."

1. No wild hits or runs, no frantic fielding; it was a... (4, 4): ___________
2. After Minnesota won the AL Central, the team picture showed many... (5, 5): ___________
3. Walk-off blast brought victory (4 3, 3): _______________
4. He loitered outside the ballpark in his shabby apparel (7, 3): ___________
5. This pitch was further outside and more obviously a ball than the prior one (5, 6): _______________
6. Team gofer's assignment to buy a piece of equipment for the catcher (4, 4): _______________
7. The manager's assertion in the interview following a loss that the umps miscalled several key plays (8, 5): _______________
8. Player's announcement to his manager upon limping into the locker room before the game (4 4, 5): ______________________
9. Touted infielder who fails to impress anybody (9, 4): _______________
10. The contest to determine the best base swiper (6 4, 4): _______________
11. Jesting about potential off-field maneuvering (5 5, 5): _______________

Answers on page 175.

What's the Score?

ATTENTION VISUAL SEARCH

Can you find the 2 scoreboards that are identical?

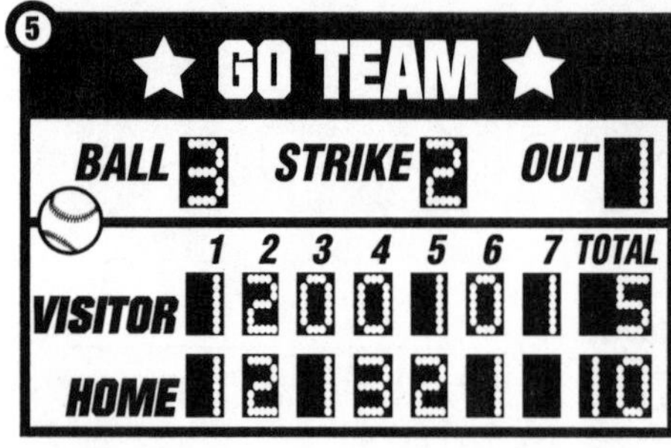

Answer on page 175.

Word Columns

LANGUAGE PLANNING

Find the hidden humorous quote from Casey Stengel by using the letters directly below each of the blank squares. Each letter is used only once. A black square indicates the end of a word, unless the word ends at the end of a row.

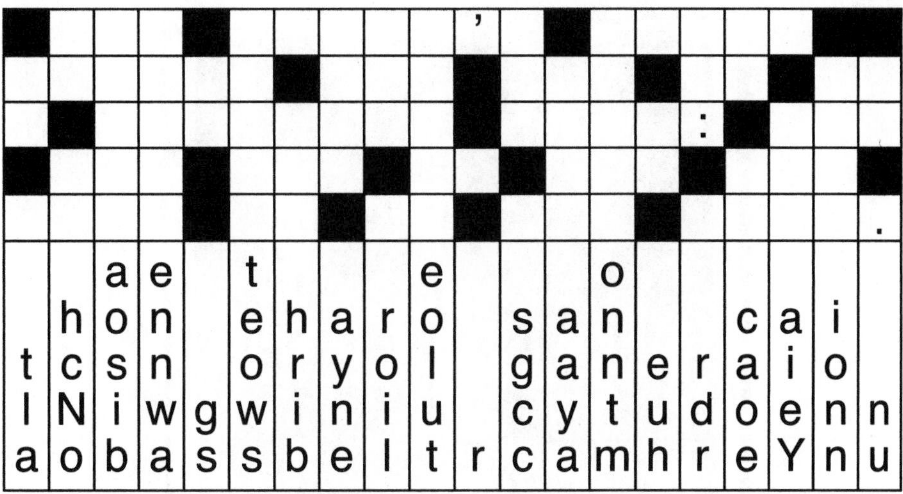

Smart Trams

ANALYSIS LOGIC

Place a letter into each box to spell one word forward and another backward.

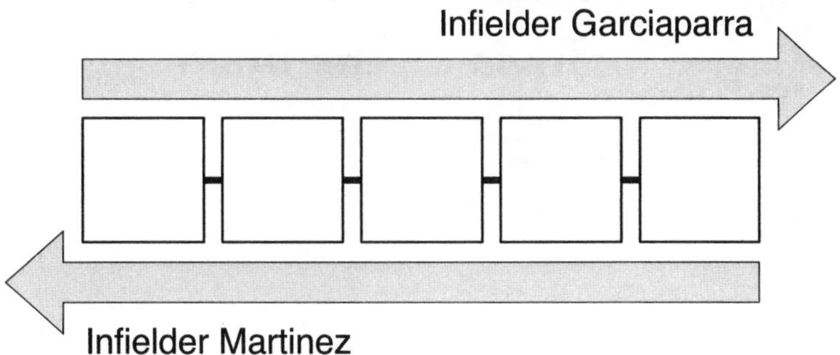

Answers on pages 175.

Chalk Talk

ANALYSIS LANGUAGE

Can you “read” the 6 baseball phrases on the chalkboard?

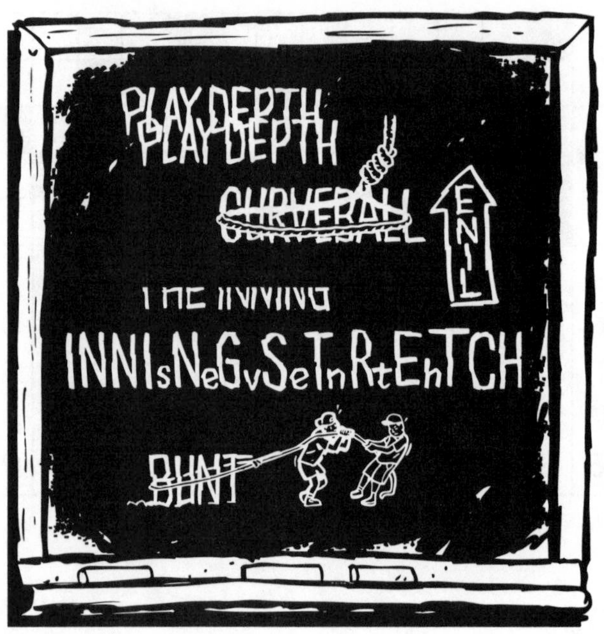

Trivia on the Brain

A baseball weighs 5 ounces and costs about $6 per ball. Major League Baseball spends about $5.5 million for baseballs every year.

Answers on page 176.

Grid Fill

LANGUAGE PLANNING

To complete this puzzle, place the given letters and words into the shapes in this grid. Words and letters will run across, down, and wrap around each shape. When the grid is filled, each row will contain one of the following words: first, fly ball, home run, out, run, stadium, teams.

1. F, H, I, L, O, T, U

2. IM, LM, MN, ST, US

3. BAD, ERA, FLY, OUR

4. STUN, TEAR

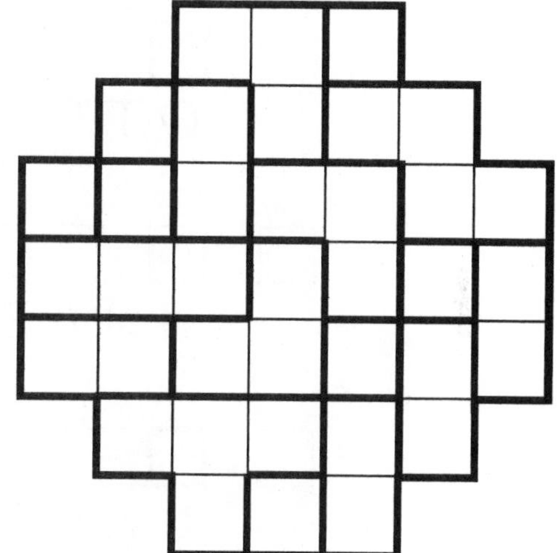

Answer on page 176.

Double Jumble

LANGUAGE

It's 2 jumbles in 1! First, unscramble the 7 letters under each row of squares to form common English words and write the words in the boxes. When you've completed the first jumble, unscramble the letters running down each column (in the dark boxes) to reveal 2 baseball-related words.

O T F F F I L

U N A B A E D

U N R O A G L

D O V A A C O

Trivia on the Brain

The most expensive baseball sold to date is Mark McGwire's 70th home run ball, which went for $3,005,000.

Answers on page 176.

Take Me Out to the Ball Game

GENERAL KNOWLEDGE

Baseball is full of crackerjack players who are better known by their nicknames than by their real ones. Can you pick out the real first names of these stars of America's pastime?

1. "Yogi" Berra:
   a) Boo-Boo
   b) Barry
   c) James
   d) Lawrence

2. "Dizzy" Dean
   a) Disraeli
   b) Ditsy
   c) Jay
   d) Joe

3. "Pepper" Martin
   a) Georgy
   b) Bobby
   c) Ronny
   d) Johnny

4. "Sparky" Anderson
   a) Sparky
   b) Andrew
   c) George
   d) Harry

5. "Bo" Jackson
   a) Beau
   b) Robert
   c) Michael
   d) Vincent

6. "Pee Wee" Reese
   a) Harold
   b) Periwinkle
   c) Peter
   d) Minnie

7. "Babe" Ruth
   a) Bambino
   b) George
   c) Babe
   d) Charles

8. "Red" Ruffing
   a) Patrick
   b) Rufus
   c) Charles
   d) Reed

9. "Catfish" Hunter
   a) Rod
   b) James
   c) Gil
   d) Tab

10. "Duke" Snider
    a) Earl
    b) Edward
    c) Prince
    d) Edwin

Answers on page 176.

ROUNDING SECOND BASE

LEVEL 3

Word Jigsaw

LANGUAGE PLANNING

Place the given letter tiles into the shapes on this pennant-shape grid. When complete, the grid will contain words that run across and down.

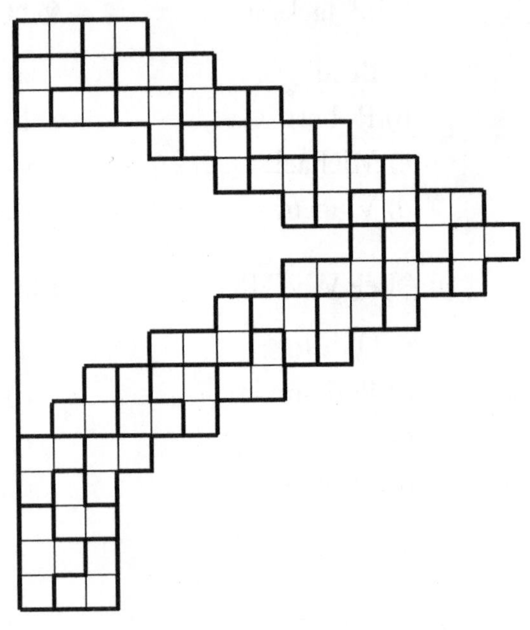

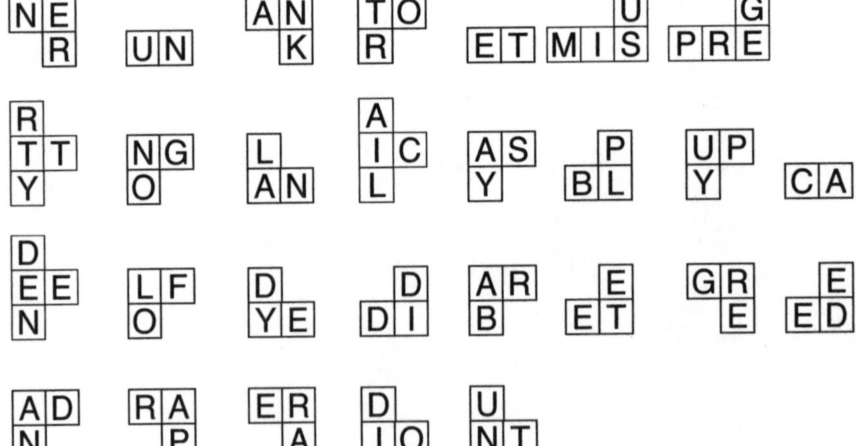

Answer on page 176.

Grid Fill

LANGUAGE PLANNING

To complete this puzzle, place the given letters and words into the shapes on this grid. Words and letters will run across, down, and wrap around each shape. When the grid is filled, each row will contain one of the following words: home run, innings, out, run, strikes, teams, walks.

1. I, K, N, R, S, W
2. AM, GS, MS, RI
3. INN, OUT, TEA
4. HOST, RULE
5. SUNKEN

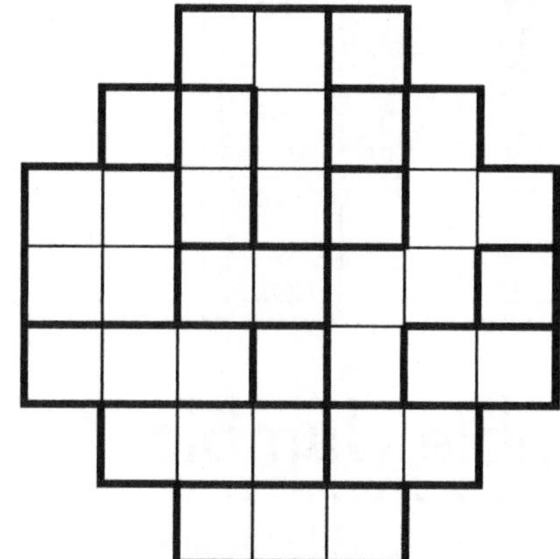

Network

ANALYSIS LOGIC

Place letters into the empty circles so that the given words can be spelled out in order from letter to consecutive letter through connected circles. Letters can be used more than once, and you can double back to a previously used letter.

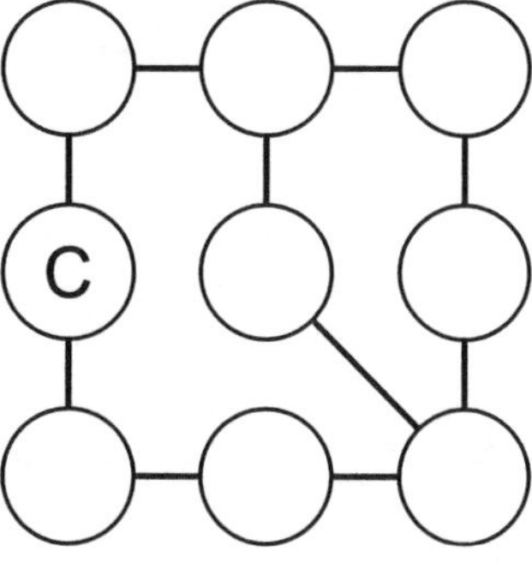

POWER PITCHER

Answers on page 176.

Name Calling

ANALYSIS

Decipher the encoded words in the baseball axiom below using the numbers and letters on the phone pad. Remember that each number can stand for 3 or 4 possible letters.

Never make the 3–4–6–2–5 out at 8–4–4–7–3.

Double Jumble

LANGUAGE

It's 2 jumbles in 1! First, unscramble the 7 letters under each row of squares to form common words, and write the words in the boxes. When you've completed the first jumble, unscramble the letters running down each column (in the dark boxes) to reveal 2 baseball-related words.

☐ ☐☐☐☐☐☐☐ ☐
I A L H E T C

☐ ☐☐☐☐☐☐☐ ☐
O A P A I T C

☐ ☐☐☐☐☐☐☐ ☐
G L E E B I L

☐ ☐☐☐☐☐☐☐ ☐
G L A D B U Y

☐ ☐☐☐☐☐☐☐ ☐
S P E L U M I

☐ ☐☐☐☐☐☐☐ ☐
U B T A L E A

Answers on pages 176–177.

Codeword

LANGUAGE ANALYSIS

The letters of the alphabet are hidden in code: They are represented by a number from 1 through 26. With the letters already given, complete the crossword puzzle and break the code. When you do, you'll discover the last names of nine 2009 National League All-Stars.

17	10	6	6	15	12	4	■	1	16	1	3	2
■	14	■	14	■	8	■	2	■	14	■	24	■
11	20	15	20	17	25	■	20	16	1	15	12	23
■	9	■	9	■	20	■	15	■	5	■	14	■
14	25	12	1	■	16	1	4	20	15	1	9	12
■	13	■	19	■	20	■	■	■	■	■	21	■
■	■	22	20	3	13	6	14	20	15	6	■	■
■	18	■	■	■	■	■	1	■	6	■	19	■
24	20	15	3	12	3	5	19	■	19	12	6	10
■	26	■	24	■	1	■	20	■	20	■	24	■
18	5	7	6	24	17	■	14	1	15	3	20	4
■	12	■	22	■	25	■	12	■	1	■	15	■
5	13	24	12	21	■	1	23	1	24	12	1	17

1	2	3	4	5	6	7	8	9	10	11	12	13
		C			O						E	

14	15	16	17	18	19	20	21	22	23	24	25	26
								V		L		

Answer on page 177.

Pic-a-Pix

ANALYSIS LOGIC

Use the clues on the left of every row and the top of every column to reveal the picture hidden in the grid below. Numbers indicate how many blocks get colored in, and the sequence in which they get colored. There must be at least one empty block between each sequence.

Column clues (left to right):

Column	Clue
1	5
2	2 2 4
3	1 3 2 2 2
4	6 2 1 1 1
5	6 1 2 1 1
6	6 1 3 2
7	6 1 4
8	7
9	7
10	7
11	4 6
12	7 6
13	8 5
14	9 4
15	10 4
16	8 1 4
17	9 5
18	4 1 4
19	8 3
20	7 3

Row clues (top to bottom):

Row	Clue
1	3 5
2	2 2 7
3	1 4 7 2
4	1 5 7 2
5	1 6 10
6	2 6 9
7	2 6 9
8	2 6 8
9	2 6 2 1 2
10	1 5 5
11	7
12	5
13	5
14	4 4
15	2 3 4
16	1 1 2 4
17	1 1 1 4
18	2 2 5
19	4 4
20	4

Answer on page 177.

Baseball Homes Letterbox

LOGIC PLANNING

The letters in ARIZONA can be found in boxes 2, 3, 5, 8, 14, and 16 but not necessarily in that order. Similarly, the letters in all the other baseball homes can be found in the boxes indicated. Your task is to insert all the letters of the alphabet into the boxes. If you do this correctly, the shaded cells will reveal another baseball home.

Hint: Compare TEXAS to SEATTLE to find the value of **X,** then TEXAS to BALTIMORE for the value of **S.**

1	2	3	4	5	6	7	8	9	10	11	12	13
14	15	16	17	18	19	20	21	22	23	24	25	26
											J	Q

ARIZONA: 2, 3, 5, 8, 14, 16

ATLANTA: 2, 3, 19, 23

BALTIMORE: 2, 5, 6, 8, 12, 14, 17, 19, 23

CHICAGO: 2, 5, 7, 8, 15, 20

CLEVELAND: 2, 3, 4, 6, 15, 22, 23

FLORIDA: 2, 4, 5, 8, 14, 21, 23

HOUSTON: 1, 3, 8, 11, 19, 20

MILWAUKEE: 2, 5, 6, 10, 11, 17, 18, 23

NEW YORK: 3, 6, 8, 10, 14, 18, 24

OAKLAND: 2, 3, 4, 8, 10, 23

PITTSBURGH: 1, 5, 7, 11, 12, 13, 14, 19, 20

ST. LOUIS: 1, 5, 8, 11, 19, 23

SEATTLE: 1, 2, 6, 19, 23

TEXAS: 1, 2, 6, 9, 19

Answers on page 177.

Missing Connections

LANGUAGE PLANNING

It's a crossword without the clues! Use the letters below to fill in the empty spaces in the crossword grid. When you are finished, you'll have words that read both across and down, crossword-style.

A E E E G G I L L L L M N O P R R S S Y

Trivia on the Brain

In the great American pastime, it's not an American with the world record for the most home runs in a career. Sadaharu Oh, of the Tokyo Giants, hit 868 homers during his 22-year career in Japan.

Answer on page 177.

Fitting Words

GENERAL KNOWLEDGE PLANNING

In this miniature crossword, the clues are listed randomly and are numbered for convenience only. It is up to you to figure out the placement of the 9 answers. To help you, we've inserted one letter in the grid, and this is the only occurrence of that letter in the completed puzzle.

1. Players on the diamond
2. Beer mug
3. Language quirk
4. Quotable catcher Berra
5. Smooch
6. Famous last word
7. Homeland of Barack Obama's father
8. Burn slightly
9. Prepare for publication

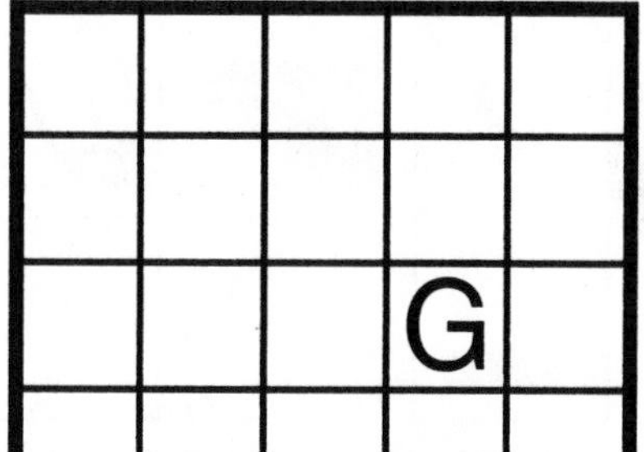

Word Jigsaw

LANGUAGE PLANNING

Fit the pieces into the frame to form common words reading across and down. There's no need to rotate the pieces; they'll fit as shown, with each piece used exactly once. As an added bonus, one of the 9 words will be the last name of a famous Chicago Cub.

S E
Y E
S O
A D
S O
N D
A M
R A

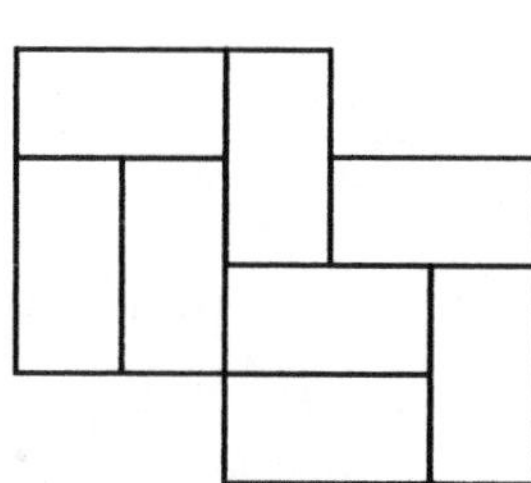

Answers on page 177.

Picture This

SPATIAL REASONING | VISUAL LOGIC

Place each of the 16 boxes in the 6 by 4 grid so they form an image of a pitcher in his windup. Do this without cutting the page apart: Use only your eyes. Eight boxes will remain blank.

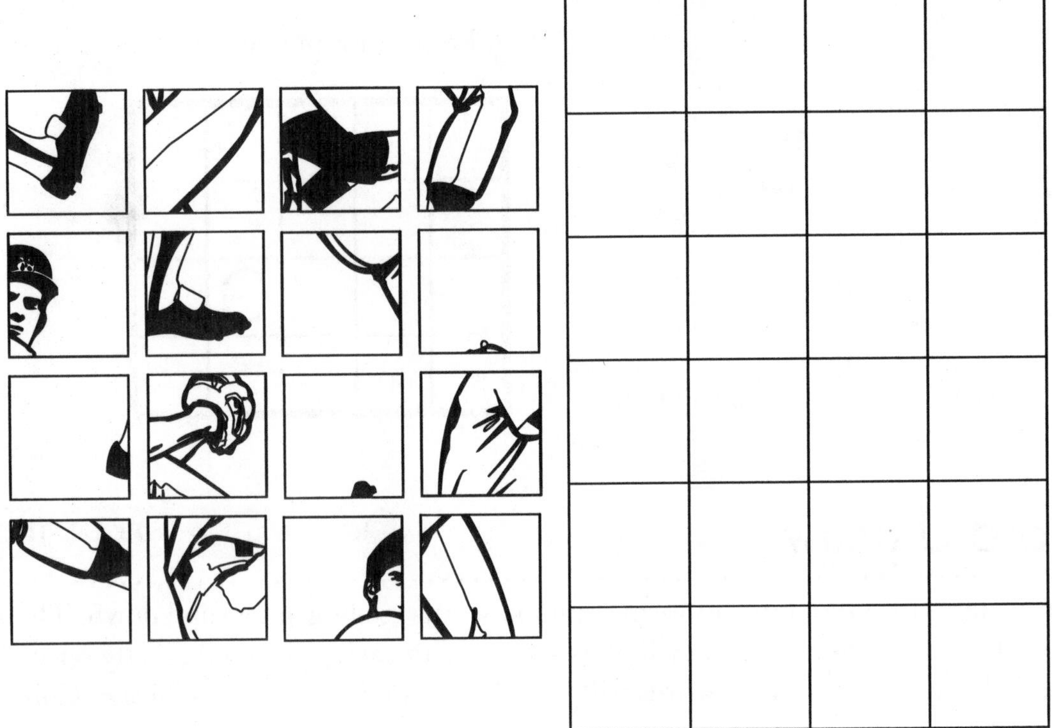

Trivia on the Brain

Jimmy Piersall disavowed the 1957 movie *Fear Strikes Out*, which claimed to be his true story, because he said it was a distortion of the facts.

Answer on page 177.

Level 3

Rhyme Time

GENERAL KNOWLEDGE | LANGUAGE

Each clue leads to a 2-word answer that rhymes, such as BIG PIG or STABLE TABLE. The numbers in parentheses after the clue give the number of letters in each word of the answer. For example, "cookware taken from the oven (3, 3)" would be "hot pot."

1. What rain might do to a baseball game (5, 4): ______________
2. A cold Philadelphia ballplayer (6, 7): ____________________
3. What a pitcher does to be taken out of a game (7, 4): ________________
4. What a manager with only left and center fielders has (5, 6): ______________
5. A group of happy supporters for the winning team (5, 5): _______________
6. A pitcher in the minors (4, 3): ________________
7. The plague on the Cubs, in comparison to the one broken by the Red Sox (5, 5): ___________________
8. A pitcher heading to his place on the field (5, 5): ___________________
9. The "tools of ignorance," to a pro catcher (6, 4): _____________________
10. A sharply hit ball (3, 4): _______________
11. A player who's spent a long time on a New York club (3, 3): ___________________

Answers on page 178.

RBI Players

LOGIC

Five teammates had a phenomenal month. Their hitting has been pivotal to the team's current winning streak. All 5 had a significant increase in their RBI totals. Using the following information, determine the full name of each player (one first name is Mike and one last name is Case) and their current number of RBIs.

First Name	Last Name	Current RBI

1. Sam Waverly didn't have an RBI total of 40.
2. Jack's RBI total was 2 more than Mr. Templeton's, and 2 fewer than Mr. Short's.
3. The 2 players with RBI totals in the 30s were Mr. Emerald and Clark.
4. Dan had the highest RBI total with 44.

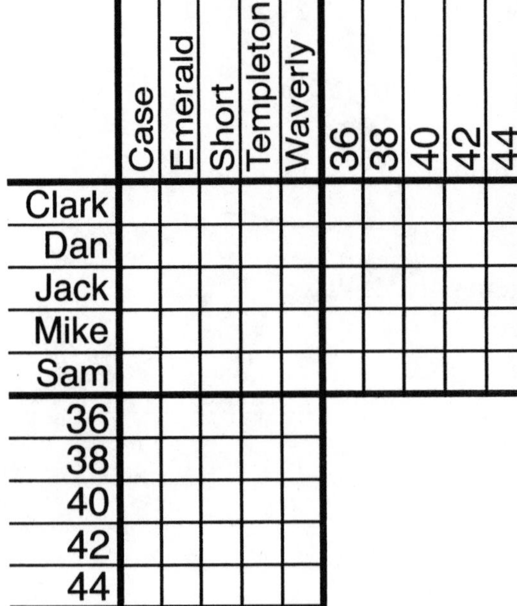

Answer on page 178.

Codeword

LANGUAGE ANALYSIS

The letters of the alphabet are hidden in code: They are represented by a number from 1 through 26. With the letters already given, complete the crossword puzzle and break the code. When you do, you'll discover the last names of nine 2009 American League All-Stars.

24	18	10			12	25	7	6	5	24	13	19
11		13		16		23		19		25		11
6	19	14	24	6	5	11		1	11	24	11	18
22		19		4		22		14		24		15
11	25	9	5	11		11	25	18	20	6	9	
6			6			3		11		11		12
18	13	2	11	3				15	11	18	7	25
25		13		26		8			9			5
	3	14	8	14	21	6		12	13	24	11	5
13		26		25		18		6		12		25
7	25	14	11	18		17	13	5	13	18	11	15
6		11		11		13		5		13		25
24	14	24	13	18	6	19	9			2	25	10

A B C D E F G H I J K L M N O P Q R S T U V W X Y Z

1	2	3	4	5	6	7	8	9	10	11	12	13
				L	I					E		

14	15	16	17	18	19	20	21	22	23	24	25	26

Answer on page 178.

Ball Games

GENERAL KNOWLEDGE | LANGUAGE

ACROSS

1. Designate
4. Oil-burning light
8. It keeps the oxen together
12. Last word of the Pledge of Allegiance
13. One of the Muses
14. Winged Greek god
15. Ancestor of baseball
17. Air ball, e.g.
18. Marquette's title
19. "It's becoming clear"
21. Olympic sport since 1988
27. Diving bird
28. Heart medication
29. Lobbying group
32. Network connections
34. The wild blue yonder
35. Gasoline brand
37. Waffle topper
39. Game in which the target is called a "jack"
42. Lacking quality
43. Rainforest tree
46. Kind of camp
48. Canada's national summer sport
52. Leia's twin brother

53. Rubber stamp
54. "Don't open _____ Xmas"
55. Even scores
56. Passenger list entry
57. Sugary liquid

DOWN

1. Protective ground cover
2. Lotion additive
3. Speak suddenly
4. Type of TV screen
5. Alcoholic beverage
6. Former space station
7. Assume as a given
8. Mocha citizen
9. Points in the right direction
10. Puts on the canvas: abbr.
11. Double twist
16. Talk-radio host Boortz
20. Martial-arts instructor
22. Pygmy chimpanzee
23. London facility
24. Provide financial support for
25. Drive to distraction
26. Protein source
29. Crony
30. Physicians for Responsible Negotiations org.
31. Ranch hand
33. House alternation
36. $100 bills
38. Not taken in by
40. Acrylic
41. Tales of adventure
44. Where many Indians live
45. Form of seaweed
46. Club alternative, briefly
47. Nice affirmative
49. Sometimes called: abbr.
50. Motion transformer
51. Sandwich-bread choice

Code-doku

LANGUAGE LOGIC

						K		
	G			F				I
Y	N		O					
I	F			U				Y
		Y		K		S		
U				S			I	O
O					K		F	N
				I			G	
		G						

Solve this puzzle just as you would a sudoku. Use deductive logic to complete the grid so that each row, column, and 3 by 3 box contains the letters FGIKNOSUY. When you have completed the puzzle, unscramble those 9 letters to reveal the last names of 2 baseball Hall of Famers.

Last names: ______________________

Answers on page 178.

Double Jumble

LANGUAGE

It's 2 jumbles in 1! First, unscramble the 7 letters under each row of squares to form common English words and write the words in the boxes. When you've completed the first jumble, unscramble the letters running down each column (in the dark boxes) to reveal 2 baseball-related words.

L A U Q N U E

B L O G A M U

Y E R I A H W

B C O O N R C

L A O T I B D

E H C A U T A

Answers on page 178.

Yer Out!

PLANNING | SPATIAL REASONING

Can you guide the path of the ball to the fielder's mitt?

Answer on page 178.

Diamond Detective

ANALYSIS LOGIC

There should be 6 words listed below; can you determine the missing fourth word? The words are connected in some way. Study the given words and letter placements carefully.

C R Y P T I C

L O Y A L

E Y E D R O P

____

A L L E G E

I S O S C E L E S

Which of these is the missing word?

RAIDS

DIALS

DAISY

DAIRY

DAILY

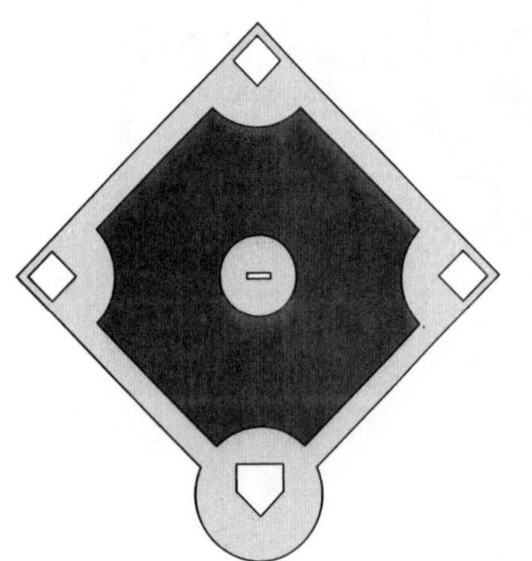

Answer on page 179.

Get Yer Peanuts!

ATTENTION | VISUAL SEARCH

Which silhouette matches the peanut vendor exactly?

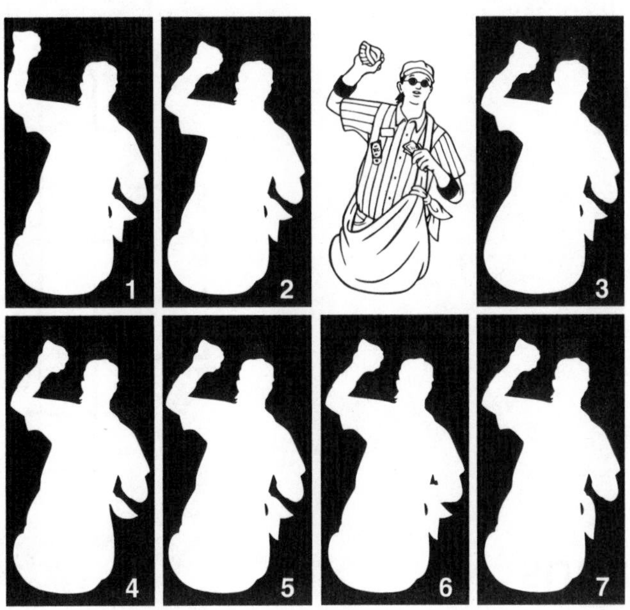

It's a Spiritual Thing

LANGUAGE | LOGIC

Cryptograms are messages in substitution code. Break the code to read the movie quote, the name of the character who spoke it, and the name of the movie. For example, THE SMART CAT might become FVO QWGDF JGF if **F** is substituted for **T, V** for **H, O** for **E,** and so on.

"N'DO QCNOP 'OU RMM, N CORMMK FRDO, RSP QFO ISMK ZFBCZF QFRQ QCBMK TOOPL QFO LIBM, PRK NS, PRK IBQ, NL QFO ZFBCZF IT VRLOVRMM."

—RSSNO LRDIK NS "VBMM PBCFRU"

Answers on page 179.

Grid Fill

LANGUAGE PLANNING

To complete this puzzle, place the given letters and words into the shapes on this grid. Words and letters will run across, down, and wrap around each shape. When the grid is filled, each row will contain one of the following words: balls, bat, dugouts, glove, run, stadium, umpires.

1. B, B, I, L, O, S, S, U

2. LO, RE, TE, UN, US

3. DUG, LID, SUM, TAG, VAT

4. RAMP

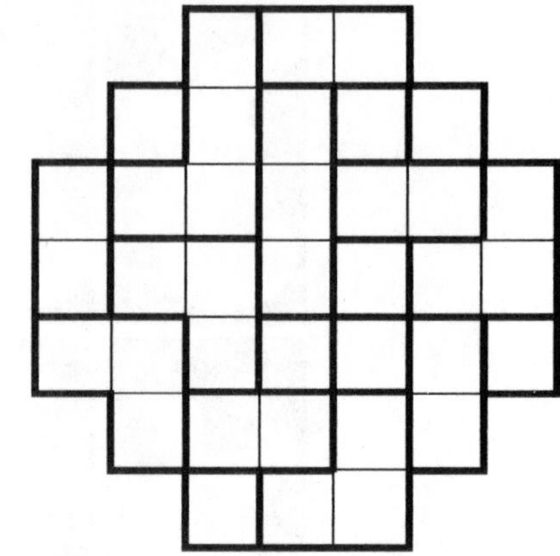

Word Columns

LANGUAGE PLANNING

Find the hidden quote from Casey Stengel by using the letters directly below each of the blank squares. Each letter is used only once. A black square indicates the end of a word, unless the word ends at the end of a row.

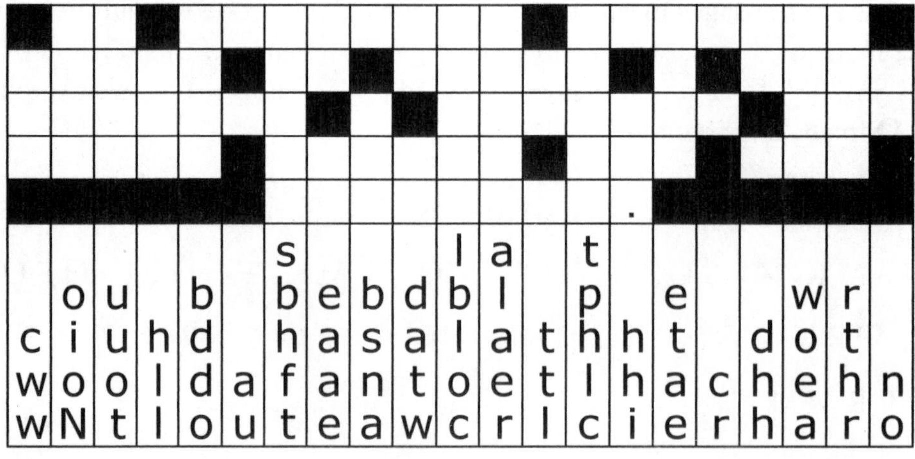

Answers on page 179.

Baseball and the White House (Part I)

MEMORY

Read these facts about baseball and presidents, then turn the page to see how much you recall.

The first president to throw out an opening-day pitch was William Howard Taft, on April 14, 1910. He threw it to Walter Johnson in a game between the Senators and the Athletics.

Ken Griffey Jr. hit the most home runs during the Clinton administration. He hit 351 homers from 1993 through 2000, while Sammy Sosa had 349 and Mark McGwire had 334 during the same period.

Lyndon Johnson was the first president to attend the dedication of a new stadium. He went to the opening of the Astrodome in Houston in 1965.

Before he was president, Ronald Reagan portrayed pitcher Grover Cleveland Alexander in the 1952 movie *The Winning Team.*

The first president to attend a World Series game was Woodrow Wilson. He attended the second game of the 1915 World Series and threw out the first pitch. (Philadelphia beat Boston 2–1.)

President Harry S. Truman attended the most major league games—16—while serving as president.

Baseball and the White House (Part II)

MEMORY

(Don't read this until you've read the previous page.)

Based on what you recall from the previous page, answer the following questions.

1. True or false: The first president to attend a World Series game was Grover Cleveland.
2. Who attended the most major league games while serving as president?
3. What was Grover Cleveland Alexander's position?
4. Ken Griffey Jr. hit the most home runs during which presidential administration?
5. True or false: The first president to throw out an opening-day pitch was William Howard Taft.

Rhyme Time

GENERAL KNOWLEDGE LANGUAGE

Each clue leads to a 2-word answer that rhymes, such as BIG PIG or STABLE TABLE. The numbers in parentheses after the clue give the number of letters in each word of the answer. For example, "cookware taken from the oven (3, 3)" would be "hot pot."

1. Minnesota victory (4, 3): __________
2. What some consider Wrigley's outfield wall (4, 6): __________
3. A Major Leaguer who has trouble beating out grounders (4, 3): __________
4. A walk-off home run (4, 5): __________
5. A pitcher coming into the game for Phillies great Carlton (7, 5): __________
6. Talent on the mound (4, 5): __________
7. A mania for Oakland's team (2, 5): __________

Answers on page 179.

It's Outta Here!

PLANNING

SPATIAL REASONING

Can you follow the slugger's blast to the ball's location at the top left of the maze?

Answer on page 179.

Baseball Tamagram

ANALYSIS LOGIC

Find an expression to define the illustration below, and then rearrange the letters of it to form an 8-letter word meaning "subject to change in size." LLL, for example, is THREE L'S, which is an anagram of SHELTER.

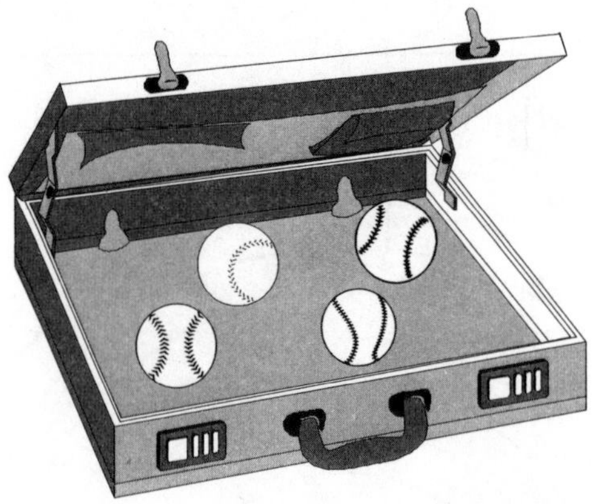

Fitting Words

GENERAL KNOWLEDGE PLANNING

In this miniature crossword, the clues are listed randomly and are numbered for convenience only. It is up to you to figure out the placement of the 9 answers. To help you, we've inserted one letter in the grid, and this is the only occurrence of that letter in the completed puzzle.

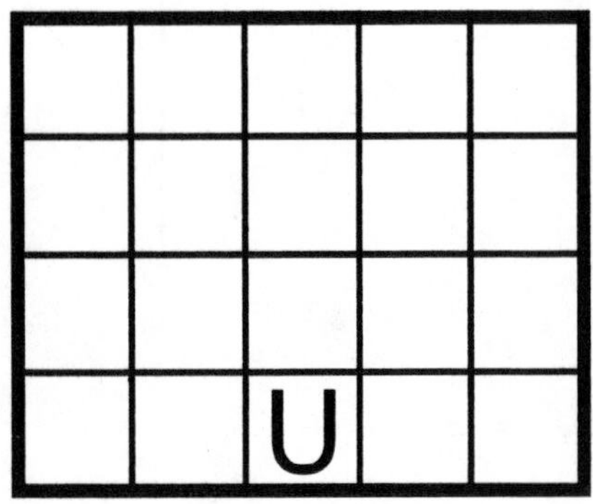

1. Pitcher's place
2. Race with batons
3. Baseball's Moises or Felipe
4. Took a gander at
5. Baseball transaction
6. Streetcar
7. Make over
8. Cherish
9. "Doggone it!"

Answers on page 179.

It's Like Déjà Vu... (Part I)

MEMORY

Study these baseball-related images for one minute, then turn the page for a memory challenge.

Batter

Ace pitcher

Mitt

Catcher

Hot dog

Baseball diamond

Baseball cap

Baseball

It's Like Déjà Vu... (Part II)

MEMORY

(Don't read this until you've read the previous page.)

Circle the names of the images you recall from the previous page.

Baseball diamond	Baseball cap	Hot dog
Joe DiMaggio	Mitt	Third baseman
Ballpark peanuts	Babe Ruth	Cold soda
Batter	Bat boy	

Baseball Quirks

LANGUAGE LOGIC

Cryptograms are messages in substitution code. Break the code to read the humorous baseball quote and its speaker. For example, THE SMART CAT might become FVO QWGDF JGF if **F** is substituted for **T**, **V** for **H**, **O** for **E**, and so on.

"DEF 'RARVXOD' EPR SXASTX CPAU FAG'OX JETCHPV EMAGJ MEDXMETT. DEF 'MOEKXD' EPR JYXF EDC, 'UYEJ OXDXOKEJHAP?' DEF 'OXRD' EPR JYXF JYHPC AN LAWWGPHDW. DEF 'SEROXD' EPR JYXF TAAC EOAGPR NAO E SOHXDJ."

—JAWWF TEDAORE

Answers on page 179.

Ted's Trophies

ATTENTION VISUAL SEARCH

Each row of Ted's trophies (horizontal, vertical, and diagonal) has one thing in common. Find each, and maybe you'll earn a trophy as well!

Word Ladder

LANGUAGE PLANNING

Using the clues along the way, change just one letter on each line to go from the top word to the bottom word. Do not change the order of the letters. You must have a common English word at each step.

HOME

_______ sharpen

____

_______ a piece

____

_______ step, on a ladder

RUNS

Answers on page 180.

MLB Records

GENERAL KNOWLEDGE

LANGUAGE

ACROSS

1. Former home run king McGwire
5. On the _____ (fleeing)
8. Cy Young has the most in MLB history
12. _____ vera (natural soother)
13. Billy Martin's retired uniform number
14. Square footage
15. Barry Bonds has the most in MLB history
17. Doe's baby
18. Muscle definition
19. King Kong, e.g.
21. Cut and paste
24. Coffee allure
28. _____ mitzvah
30. Fly like an eagle
32. _____ capita income
33. Joe DiMaggio has the longest in MLB history
36. "Much _____ About Nothing"
37. Fig. on a baseball card
38. Industrious bug
39. Like an extra-inning game
41. Put through a sieve
43. Prankster's missile
45. Right-hand person
48. "Ali ____ and the Forty Thieves"
51. Walter Johnson has the most in MLB history
55. Former Tigers shortstop and manager Trammell

56. "For _____ a jolly. . . "
57. Granny
58. Pete Rose has the most in MLB history
59. Vote of assent
60. Grand _____ (four-run shot)

DOWN

1. _____-jongg
2. "Thanks _____!"
3. Cowboys quarterback Tony
4. Most perceptive
5. Manager Piniella
6. Raggedy doll (female)
7. Flat formation
8. Necco candy piece
9. Nest-egg letters
10. _____ York Knights ("The Natural" team)
11. _____ Diego Chicken (baseball mascot debuting in 1977)
16. Rose's color, for most of his career
20. Go splitsville
22. "Money _____ everything!"
23. Frat party wear
25. Play game one of a series
26. Vegan's no-no
27. Genesis boat
28. _____ one's time (wait)
29. "This must weigh _____!"
31. Italian bubbly
33. _____ trick (hockey feat)
34. Words of understanding
35. GI food
40. Stretches across
42. Jack Sprat's taboo
44. Visibly pale
46. Like a Jekyll-Hyde personality
47. Sicilian spewer
48. Outburst from Scrooge
49. He dethroned Foreman
50. Roy Hobbs's "Wonderboy"
52. Front end of a bray
53. Springsteen's "Born in the _____"
54. Baseball great Crawford or Jethroe

Breaking the Baseball Color Line

LANGUAGE LOGIC

Cryptograms are messages in substitution code. Break the code to reveal a quote from Jackie Robinson. For example, THE SMART CAT might become FVO QWGDF JGF if **F** is substituted for **T, V** for **H, O** for **E,** and so on.

"ATU QVSTA BJ UKUQM FWUQVPFH AB JVQIA-PRFII PVAVOUHITVZ VI ATU WBIA VWZBQAFHA VIIYU BJ BYQ AVWU."

Answers on page 180.

Missing Connections

LANGUAGE PLANNING

It's a crossword without the clues! Use the letters below to fill in the empty spaces in the crossword grid. When you are finished, you'll have words that read both across and down, crossword-style.

A A A F H I K L L L M N N O O O S S T T W X

Trivia on the Brain

Did you know that the records for the most games won and the most games lost are held by the same pitcher? Cy Young reigns supreme with 551 and 316, respectively.

Answer on page 180.

Network

ANALYSIS LOGIC

Place letters into the empty circles so that the given words can be spelled out in order from letter to consecutive letter through connected circles. Letters can be used more than once, and you can double back to a previously used letter.

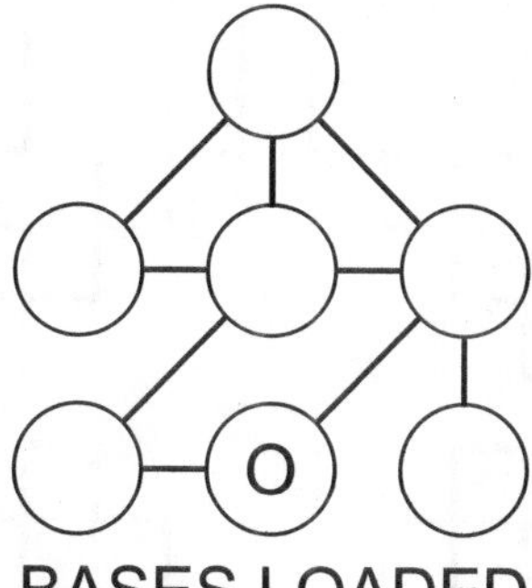

BASES LOADED

Lineup Card

ANALYSIS LOGIC

Fill in the blanks to spell out the names of great players associated with a particular team. Every occurrence of every letter of that team's name has been filled in. As a bonus, can you name the team?

1. Y ___ ___ ___ ___ e ___ ___ a

2. ___ ___ ___ ___ e ___ ___ ___ ___

3. ___ e ___ e k ___ e ___ e ___

4. ___ a ___ e ___ ___ ___ ___

5. ___ ___ e ___ ___ ___ a ___ ___ ___ ___

6. ___ ___ ___ k e y ___ a n ___ ___ e

7. ___ ___ ___ ___ ___ a n ___ ___ n s ___ n

Team: ____________________

Answers on page 180.

Word Jigsaw

LANGUAGE PLANNING

Place the given letter tiles into the shapes in this ballpark-shape grid. When complete, the grid will contain words that run across and down.

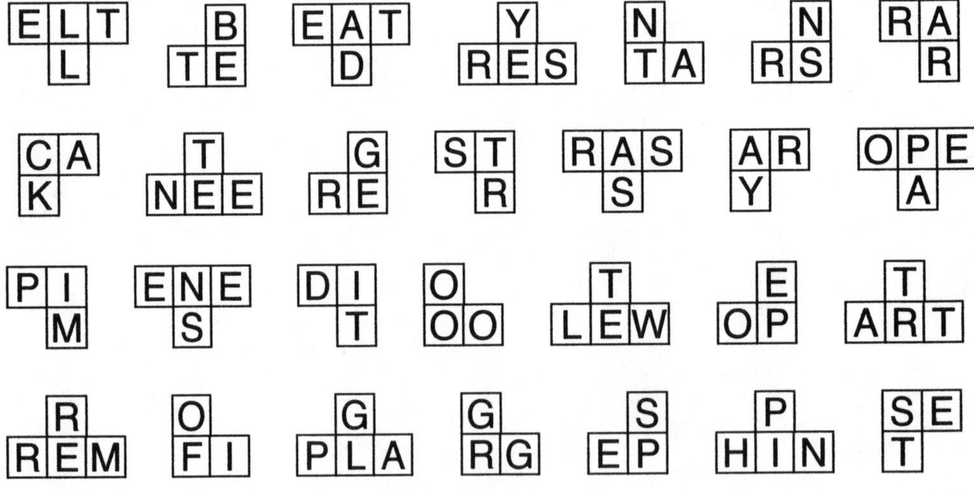

Answer on page 180.

Double Jumble

LANGUAGE

It's 2 jumbles in 1! First, unscramble the 7 letters under each row of squares to form common English words and write the words in the boxes. When you've completed the first jumble, unscramble the letters running down each column (in the dark boxes) to reveal 2 baseball-related words.

N A R G O E O

S L I S E N L

A I G L R A E

K E N U K L C

O N C E L E H

I S O U B O V

Trivia on the Brain

Some players consider it bad luck if a dog happens to walk across the diamond before the first pitch.

Answers on page 180.

Word Ladder

LANGUAGE PLANNING

Using the clues along the way, change just one letter on each line to go from the top word to the bottom word. Do not change the order of the letters. You must have a common English word at each step.

SPIT

______

______ dove foot-first toward a base

______ uttered

______

______ leave abruptly

BALL

Hidden Ball Trick

ANALYSIS PLANNING

Locate balls hidden in these gloves. Each arrow points to only one ball in that row, and each ball is pointed to by only one arrow. Balls are not found in neighboring gloves.

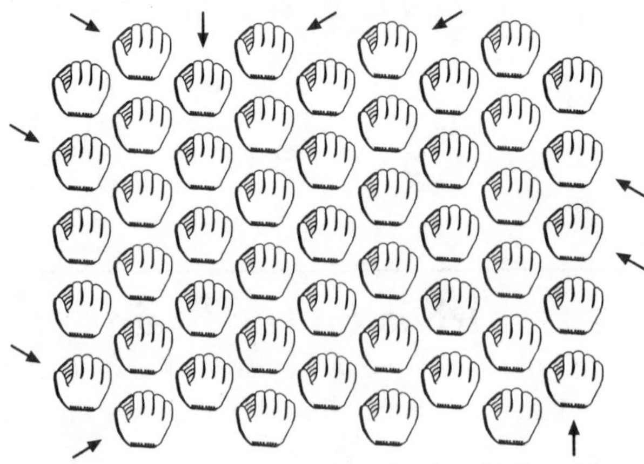

Answers on pages 181.

Codeword

ANALYSIS LANGUAGE

The letters of the alphabet are hidden in code: They are represented by a number from 1 through 26. With the letters already given, complete the crossword puzzle and break the code. When you do, you'll discover the last names of 9 players who were on the 2009 L.A. Dodgers roster.

6	19	5	11	16	9	■	17	16	18	5	5	18
26	■	19	■	9	■	20	■	9	■	8	■	11
22	26	6	■	3	20	8	26	11	■	26	24	13
3	■	16	■	13	■	9	■	5	■	9	■	16
20	25	5	18	■	5	18	2	16	9	23	20	18
18	■	18	■	19	■	25	■	24	■	■	■	5
■	8	21	8	9	18	■	4	26	6	1	8	■
16	■	■	■	19	■	19	■	18	■	5	■	2
11	5	8	9	3	8	22	8	■	11	8	10	26
22	■	5	■	8	■	17	■	6	■	12	■	5
18	9	23	■	9	19	16	14	18	■	11	15	8
20	■	18	■	23	■	3	■	9	■	8	■	23
10	26	5	3	19	20	■	7	26	19	9	11	19

A B C D E F G H I J K L M N O P Q R S T U V W X Y Z

1	2	3	4	5	6	7	8	9	10	11	12	13
				R								

14	15	16	17	18	19	20	21	22	23	24	25	26
				E		L					Y	

Answer on page 181.

Idioms from the Diamond

LANGUAGE

ACROSS

1. Movie snippet
5. Minor leagues
10. Henry R. or Clare Booth
14. Climber's goal
15. Underway
16. Spanish "ones"
17. One-time Korean president
18. Bath scrubber
19. Up to the task
20. Guesstimate
23. Jockey, perhaps
24. Scotch partner
25. Army div.
27. Medical grp.
28. NASDAQ relative
31. Actor Watanabe
33. Pastoral poet
37. Excoriate
38. Problem-solver

41. "With _____ ring I thee..."
42. Casts off, as skin
43. Bulb info
45. Greek cross
46. Vinaigrette ingredient
49. Thunder Bay prov.
50. McConaughey–Elfman film, 1999
54. Cisneros's "The House on _____ Street"
56. Ensure safety; prepare thoroughly
60. Actress Ryan ("Star Trek: Voyager")
61. Fred's dancing partner
62. Tatamis, e.g.
63. Shrinking sea
64. Coffeehouse choice
65. Sculptor Nadelman
66. Costar of Clooney and Margulies
67. Welcome to one's house
68. Certain volleyball shots

DOWN

1. Headlights protector?
2. Hebrew toast
3. British actress Staunton
4. "The Old Wives' Tale" playwright
5. F.D.R.'s Scottie
6. Get an _____ effort
7. Movable castles
8. Soprano Anna
9. Proper and decorous
10. Waikiki wingding
11. Free from restraint
12. Its days are numbered
13. Oakland-to-Vegas dir.
21. Big name in handbags
22. Borscht Belt bit
26. "30 Rock" creator
29. Roget entries: abbr.
30. 12th month, in Israel
32. Young newts
33. Superlative suffix
34. Dot-com's desire
35. Word in Kubrick's final film
36. Pulau _____ ("Survivor" island)
38. Diocese office
39. Of the seashore
40. Hitchhike
41. Tangoing number
44. Call at poker
46. Clearance sign
47. Joke response
48. Red-ink figures
51. Type of queen
52. Fusses
53. Like some blouses
55. Willie of "Eight Is Enough"
57. Wretchedly bad
58. Grades 1–12, for short
59. Actor Connery
60. Chew the fat

Answers on page 181.

Bang-Bang Play

ATTENTION VISUAL SEARCH

It's a close call, but which 2 of these exciting plays at the plate are exactly alike?

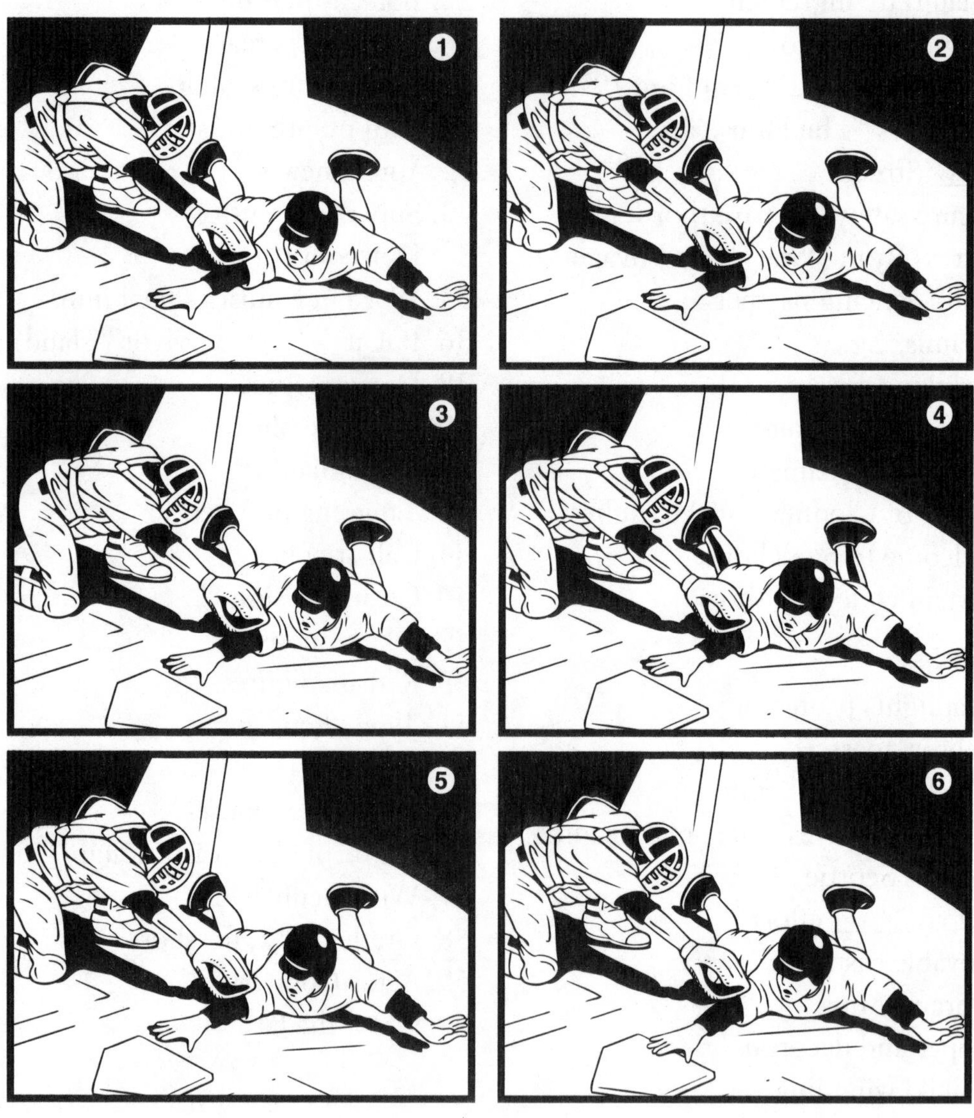

Answer on page 181.

Left, Right, and Center

ATTENTION VISUAL SEARCH

Every name listed below is contained within the group of letters. Names can be found in a straight line horizontally, vertically, or diagonally. They may be read either forward or backward. When complete, the leftover letters will spell a quote from George Will.

As an added bonus, can you name the player on the list who was on the original roster of the New York Mets?

```
C O R S N I D E R R E C T T H
I N K N R E N M R S T H I N K
T H Y U A O T B A S H B U R N
A W T S S E S B A N L W B L P
G H I K T R T O I V T I I O U
A E C N O R A A I R E L Y U C
I A L S F A R N S G O L E X K
J T A Y M I G P O R G I O N E
N O I K S M E Z R T S A Y T T
H I S N A A L L S Y A M M G T
A B U O K L L U D T B S A I S
E B M E D W I C K O A L L I D
S T R O U S H N R I B R O C K
N O S L I W A N E R V Y I A L
```

AARON
ASHBURN
BROCK
COBB
CUYLER
DIMAGGIO
DOBY
GWYNN
JACKSON
KALINE
MANTLE
MAYS
MEDWICK
MUSIAL
PUCKETT
ROUSH
RUTH
SNIDER
SPEAKER
STARGELL
WANER
WHEAT
WILLIAMS
WILSON
WINFIELD
YASTRZEMSKI

Leftover letters: ______________________________

____

Original player: ______________________

Answers on page 181.

SLIDING INTO THIRD BASE

LEVEL 4

Word Jigsaw

LANGUAGE PLANNING

Place the given letter tiles into the diamond-shape grid to form common words. When complete, words will run across and down, crossword style.

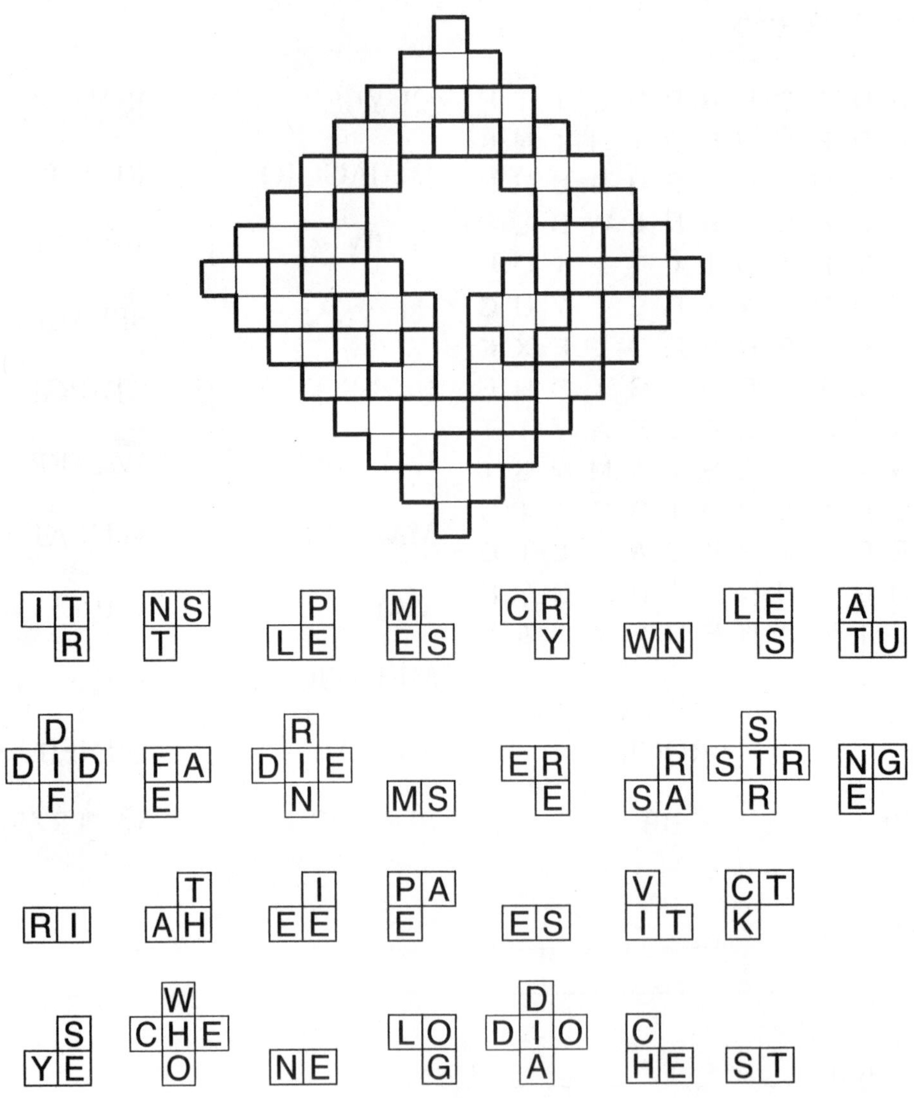

Answer on page 181.

Double Jumble

LANGUAGE

It's 2 jumbles in 1! First, unscramble the 7 letters under each row of squares to form common English words and write the words in the boxes. When you've completed the first jumble, unscramble the letters running down each column (in the dark boxes) to reveal 2 baseball-related words.

F R A C I F T

H I C A C R A

N A R G A O L

S H I M T S U

V R A D B O A

E N M I E O N

P T I U M H R

Answers on page 181.

The Name Game

GENERAL KNOWLEDGE | LANGUAGE

1	2	3	4	■	5	6	7	■	8	9	10	11
12				■	13			■	14			
15				16				■	17			
■	■	■	18				■	19				
20	21	22			■	■	23				■	■
24			■	25	26	27			■	28	29	30
31			■	■	32			■	■	33		
34			■	35				36	■	37		
■	■	38	39			■	■	40	41			
42	43				■	44	45			■	■	■
46				■	47					48	49	50
51				■	52			■	53			
54				■	55			■	56			

ACROSS

1. Nickname of pitcher Dave Righetti
5. Ballpark fig.
8. Antiquing agent
12. Sign over a ballpark gate
13. Excessively
14. El _____ (weather phenomenon)
15. MLB player-manager of 1984–86
17. Like Ernie Lombardi, on the basepaths
18. _____ cava
19. Pitcher Kyle, a Native American of the Nomlaki nation
20. Third baseman Charlie, who caught the last out of the 1996 World Series
23. Gambling mecca
24. WWII Pacific battle site, for short
25. Ruth's retired number
28. _____ Moines

31. “The Crime _____” (nickname of baseball’s Fred McGriff)
32. Cyclotron bit
33. Something to work off during spring training, maybe
34. Positive or negative molecule
35. Player sporting a halo
37. Pitching Triple Crown stat
38. Former ML commissioner _____ Giamatti
40. Firebug’s doing
42. Yankee Pee Wee _____
44. 1995 AL Rookie of the Year Hideo _____
46. Mr. Potato Head stick-ons
47. Manager with the ML record for ejections
51. Spread unit
52. Witness-stand reply
53. Perfect-game hurler David _____
54. “Neato,” updated
55. Boston NLer of the ’30s
56. Took a gander at

DOWN

1. Weight room unit
2. Send packing
3. Oater “Scram!”
4. Hall of Famer Carlton
5. School attended by 007
6. Three-time 60-homer man
7. “Turf _____” (affliction caused by playing on artificial surfaces)
8. Baseball great Cap _____
9. Manager of the 1969 Miracle Mets
10. Slaughter in Cooperstown
11. ’30s ML pitcher “Schoolboy” _____
16. It may be five days, for a starter
19. Former pitcher Bill, nicknamed “Spaceman”
20. Baseball, or baseball glove, material
21. MP’s quarry
22. Quotable player who managed the Yankees and Mets
23. Lachemann, who managed four ML teams
26. Help for the stumped
27. Baseball’s Maris, for short
29. Trevi fountain throw-in, now
30. “_____ the Man” (nickname in Cardinals history)
35. “_____ we there yet?”
36. Mild-mannered one
39. Great arm, or speed on the basepaths, say
41. _____ Clayton, who played for 11 ML teams between 1991 and 2007
42. Haul in
43. Pricing word
44. Meeting point
45. Double-reed instrument
47. Overalls part
48. Artfully shy
49. Retired number worn by Richie Ashburn and Fred Hutchinson
50. Marked the treasure map

Answers on page 182.

Picture This

SPATIAL REASONING VISUAL LOGIC

Place each of the 24 boxes in the 5 by 6 grid so they form a baseball picture that's ready for some heat. Do this without cutting the page apart: Use only your eyes. Six boxes will remain blank.

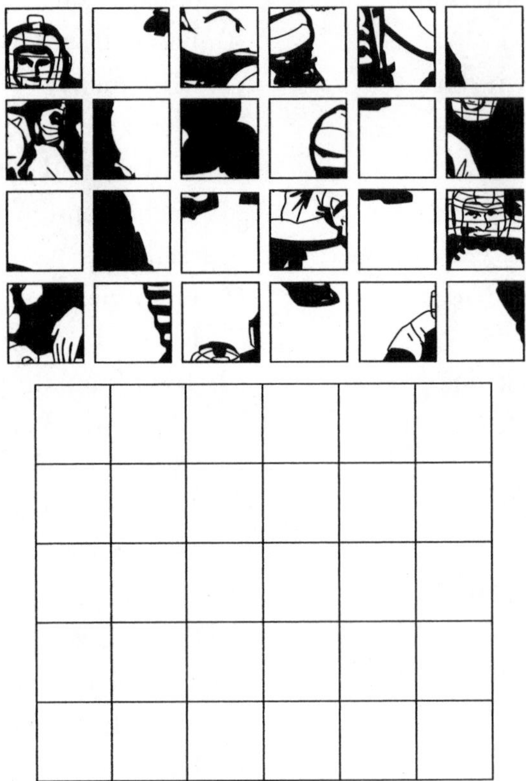

Baseball Quirks

LANGUAGE LOGIC

Cryptograms are messages in substitution code. Break the code to read the quote and its source. For example, THE SMART CAT might become FVO QWGDF JGF if **F** is substituted for **T, V** for **H, O** for **E,** and so on.

"K XCRH QWFZ QWH ULVHEUYKYKQW—YQLMX CFF YXH TCUHU DXHW K XKY C XQOH ELW."

—TCTH ELYX

Answers on page 182.

Codeword

ANALYSIS LANGUAGE

The letters of the alphabet are hidden in code: They are represented by a number from 1 through 26. With the letters already given, complete the crossword puzzle and break the code. When you do, you'll discover the last names of 9 players who were on the Atlanta Braves roster in 2009.

13	16	14	14	13	20	22	2		8	11	15	20
25		20		11		3		9		21		2
22	11	21		22	16	8	8	2		21	25	7
4		14		20		11		3		20		11
	6	23	22	2	11	22		7	23	14	11	12
		25						6				23
17	23	22	25	2	6		5	20	22	7	20	14
23				3						14		
19	11	11	18	2		9	23	15	22	20	10	
24		15		21		14		23		11		10
16	14	22		20	18	23	25	8		2	1	25
20		20		18		10		21		11		23
19	20	14	11		26	11	22	19	23	8	20	19

A B C D E F G H I J K L M N O P Q R S T U V W X Y Z

1	2	3	4	5	6	7	8	9	10	11	12	13
										O		

14	15	16	17	18	19	20	21	22	23	24	25	26
R					Z	E						

Answer on page 182.

Curveball

ANALYSIS LOGIC

Starting from each number outside the grid, draw a line leading from that number to a mitt. No lines can intersect, and the number of boxes the line passes through coincides with the number it originates from. So, if a line begins at the number 6, it must pass through 6 boxes (including the box the mitt is in). All boxes will be used.

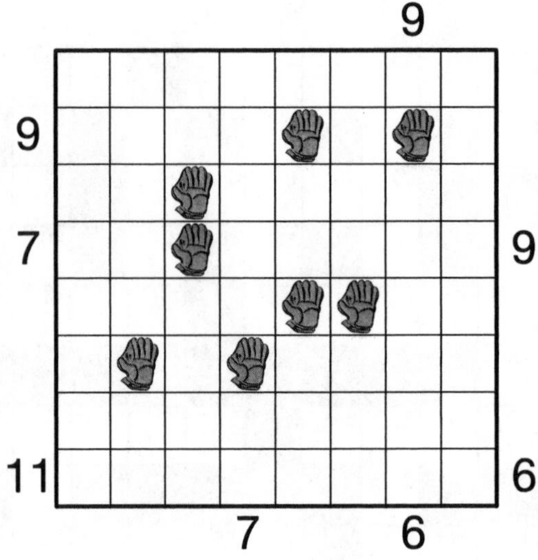

Shifter

ANALYSIS LOGIC

Solve the word for either clue, then move each letter to its new spot following the lines from one box to another.

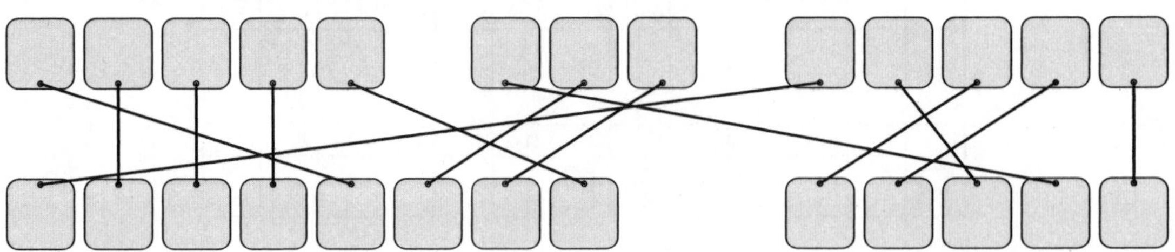

Answers on page 182.

Level 4

Hurler Hunt

ATTENTION | VISUAL SEARCH

Every pitcher listed below is contained within the group of letters. Names can be found in a straight line horizontally, vertically, or diagonally. They may be read either forward or backward. Leftover letters spell a quote from Sandy Koufax, one of baseball's greatest southpaws.

ALEXANDER	HUNTER	SUTTON	WYNN
BROWN	JENKINS	WADDELL	YOUNG
BUNNING	JOHNSON	WILHELM	
CARLTON	LEMON		
DEAN	MARICHAL		
DRYSDALE	MATHEWSON		
ECKERSLEY	MCGINNITY		
FELLER	NIEKRO		
FINGERS	PALMER		
FORD	PERRY		
GIBSON	RUFFING		
GOMEZ	RYAN		
GROVE	SEAVER		
HUBBELL	SPAHN		

```
I B Y E R E D N A X E L A C A
M S E A V E R O R K E I N E A
G G L O O N O S B I G D P I T
R C S H E R F W L R W O H E N
O I R S T O F E L L E R M P P
V E E M W I L H E L M T D E T
E R K C N Y I T D Y A B N N Z
L J C G G T O A D M R A K U E
A T E I H E M M A O I R M I H
D R N N O M E L W S C S E C U
S T A N K H E N Y B H A A P B
Y Y E I H I L L N A A R N A B
R D D T S A N T N A L R Y L E
D T E Y D T P S U T T O N M L
R Y I J O H N S O N U N G E L
T O M A B U N N I N G K E R T
H E M H I T I T G N I F F U R
```

Leftover letters: ______________________________

____

Answers on page 182.

Have a Ball

ATTENTION VISUAL SEARCH

Study the illustration below and find 8 things that, when combined with the word "ball," create a compound word or phrase.

Shifter

ANALYSIS LOGIC

Solve the word for either clue, then move each letter to its new spot following the lines from one box to another.

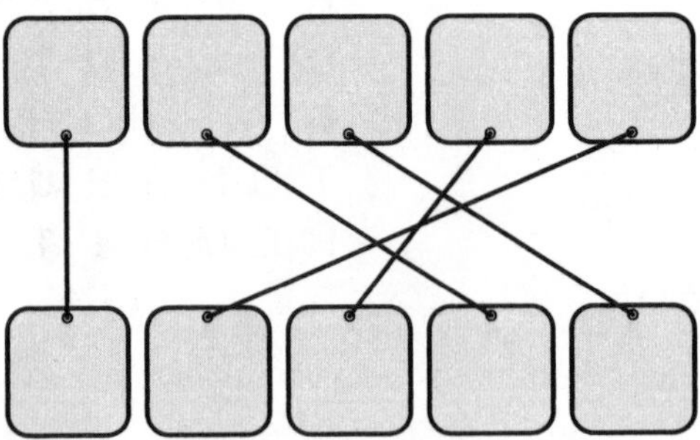

Answers on pages 182–183.

Level 4

Lineup Card

GENERAL KNOWLEDGE | LANGUAGE

Fill in the blanks to spell out the names of great players associated with a particular team. Every occurrence of every letter of that team's name has been filled in. As a bonus, can you name the team?

1. ___ ___ o r ___ ___   ___ r ___ ___ ___

2. ___ r ___ ___   ___ a ___ ___ ___

3. ___ a l   ___ ___ R a ___

4. ___ r a ___ ___   ___ ___ ___ ___ ___

5. ___ a ___   ___ ___ ___ s ___ ___ ___ ___ r r y

6. ___ o   ___ a ___ ___ s o ___

7. ___ ___ l l ___ ___   ___ ___ l s o ___

8. A ___ o s   O ___ ___ s

Team: ____________________

Network

ANALYSIS | LOGIC

Place letters into the empty circles so that the given words can be spelled out in order from letter to consecutive letter through connected circles. Letters can be used more than once, and you can double back to the same letter.

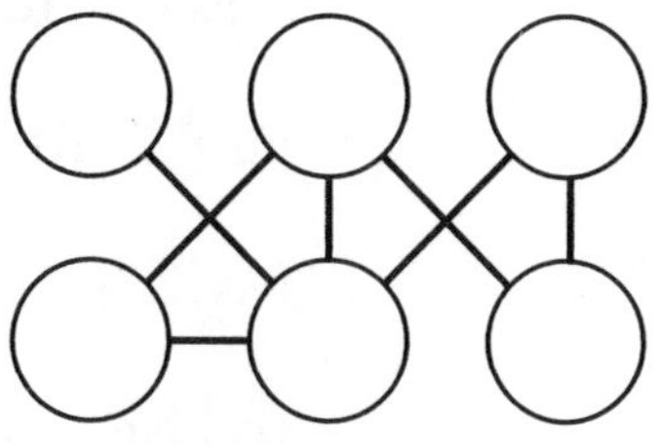

FARM TEAM

Answers on page 183.

Pinstripe Club

ATTENTION | VISUAL SEARCH

Every Yankee great listed below and at the top of the next page is contained within the group of letters. Names can be found in a straight line horizontally, vertically, or diagonally. They may be read either forward or backward. When complete, the left-over letters will spell a quote from Casey Stengel.

```
M A N A G E T T I T T E P G I
N G I S O N O S N U M A R I S
R U T H M G J A C K S O N E S
I E T T E Y L G N I T T A M I
C G N G Z H S S I L B M A H C
H A P M R E H S I W S I H M A
A S B A I N U D F O L R S H A
R S O R O D M G W L O P E Z R
D O T T E E T E I X E I R A R
S G U I D R Y W N R E R T E E
O E Z N U S A N F E D F Y S B
N H Z S O O M E I T N O M A D
O R I M A N T L E E B R R N E
E I R I V E R A L J L D S E H
I G T Y E K C I D R A W O H S
```

BERRA	DICKEY	GUIDRY	LOPEZ
BOYER	FORD	HENDERSON	MANTLE
CABRERA	GEHRIG	HOWARD	MARIS
CHAMBLISS	GOMEZ	JACKSON	MARTIN
DAMON	GOSSAGE	JETER	MATSUI

Answers on page 183.

MATTINGLY
MUNSON
PETTITTE
RICHARDSON
RIVERA
RIZZUTO
RODRIGUEZ
RUTH
SWISHER
TEIXEIRA
TRESH
WILLIAMS
WINFIELD

Leftover letters: ____

____

Code-doku

LANGUAGE LOGIC

Solve this puzzle just as you would a sudoku. Use deductive logic to complete the grid so that each row, column, and 3 by 3 box contains the letters ABHKNRSTU. When you have completed the puzzle, unscramble those 9 letters to reveal the last names of 2 baseball Hall of Famers.

					R	K		
	B			A				H
	N							
H				U				R
		R		K		S		
U							H	T
T					K		A	N
	R						B	
		B				R		

Last names: ____

Answers on page 183.

Rhyme Time

GENERAL KNOWLEDGE LANGUAGE

Each clue leads to a 2-word answer that rhymes, such as BIG PIG or STABLE TABLE. The numbers in parentheses after the clue give the number of letters in each word of the answer. For example, "cookware taken from the oven (3, 3)" would be "hot pot."

1. The Green Monster (7, 5): ______________
2. An equipment manager (6, 7): ______________
3. A skinny peanut-peddler (7, 6): ______________
4. A last-minute fielding adjustment for a pull hitter (5, 5): ______________
5. An outfielder's errant throw home to nail a scoring opponent (6, 6): ______________
6. Brewers' slugger Fielder's thin pancakes (7, 8): ______________
7. What 90 feet does in the Major Leagues (6, 5): ______________
8. A postseason reward for investment (7, 6): ______________
9. The knuckleball, for Wakefield (5, 5): ______________
10. An urchin who beats the throw to first (4, 4): ______________
11. Sandwiches belonging to a legendary Yankee catcher (5, 7): ______________
12. Less-than-rousing fan support (7, 5): ______________
13. What a tied game needs (4, 5): ______________
14. A pitcher who doesn't quite throw fastballs but doesn't quite throw curves (6, 8): ______________
15. The frame in which the deciding run is scored (7, 6): ______________

Answers on page 183.

Pic-a-Pix

ANALYSIS LOGIC

Use the clues on the left of every row and the top of every column to reveal the picture hidden in the grid below. Numbers indicate how many blocks get colored in and the sequence in which they get colored. There must be at least one empty block between each sequence.

Column	Clue
1	4 1 2
2	3 1 1 4
3	3 2 8
4	2 2 2 4
5	2 2 2 3
6	5 2 2
7	4 2 4
8	8 3 1
9	8 2 1
10	8 1 1
11	8 2 1
12	9 1 1
13	2 8 1 1
14	4 1 5 2 1
15	3 2 4 1 1
16	3 2 2 2 3 1 3
17	3 2 3 1 7
18	3 1 5 1 5
19	10 1 1 1 2
20	5 1 1 6 2
21	2 1 1
22	6 1
23	5 1
24	6 1
25	2 3 2

Row clues (top to bottom):

Row	Clue
1	5
2	7
3	7
4	5 1 1
5	8 1
6	15
7	10 3 2
8	2 9 3
9	1 1 13
10	2 1 14
11	1 1 9 5
12	2 1 1 5 1 2
13	1 1 1 1 2 1 4
14	1 1 1 3 1 1 4
15	3 1 2 3 1 4
16	1 1 3 1 4
17	1 2 1 1 4
18	1 1 2 1 2
19	1 2 1 1
20	3 13 6
21	3 2 1 1
22	4 4
23	3 3
24	4 5
25	3 3

Answer on page 183.

Strikeout Kings

ATTENTION VISUAL SEARCH

Whether they struck the batters out swinging or looking, these 26 pitchers listed below and on the next page reached the top of their field (as of 2011). Their names can be found in a straight line vertically, horizontally, or diagonally, and may read forward or backward. The leftover letters spell a quote from Reggie Jackson about the all-time strikeout leader.

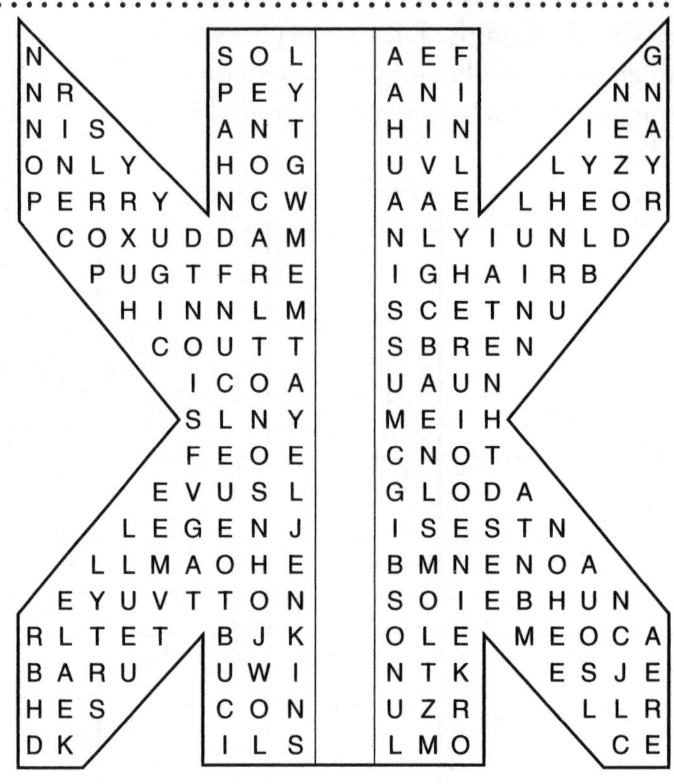

RYAN (Nolan; 5,714)

R. JOHNSON (Randy; 4,875)

CLEMENS (Roger; 4,672)

CARLTON (Steve; 4,136)

BLYLEVEN (Bert; 3,701)

SEAVER (Tom; 3,640)

SUTTON (Don; 3,574)

PERRY (Gaylord; 3,534)

W. JOHNSON (Walter; 3,508)

MADDUX (Greg; 3,371)

NIEKRO (Phil; 3,342)

JENKINS (Fergie; 3,192)

MARTINEZ (Pedro; 3,154)

GIBSON (Bob; 3,117)

SCHILLING (Curt; 3,116)

SMOLTZ (John; 3,084)

Answers on page 183.

BUNNING (Jim; 2,855)

LOLICH (Mickey; 2,832)

MUSSINA (Mike; 2,813)

YOUNG (Cy; 2,803)

TANANA (Frank; 2,773)

CONE (David; 2,668)

FINLEY (Chuck; 2,610)

GLAVINE (Tom; 2,607)

SPAHN (Warren; 2,583)

FELLER (Bob; 2,581)

Leftover letters: ____

____

Word Ladder

LANGUAGE PLANNING

Using the clues along the way, change just one letter on each line to go from the top word to the bottom word. Do not change the order of the letters. You must have a common English word at each step.

FOUL

_____ a naive person

_____

_____

_____

_____ raise up

_____

LINE

Answers on page 183.

Baseball Tamagram

ANALYSIS LOGIC

Find an expression to define the illustration below, and then rearrange the letters of it to form a 7-letter word meaning "floral." LLL, for example, is THREE L'S, which is an anagram of SHELTER.

Network

ANALYSIS LOGIC

Place letters into the empty circles so that the given words can be spelled out in order from letter to consecutive letter through connected circles. Letters can be used more than once, and you can double back to the same letter.

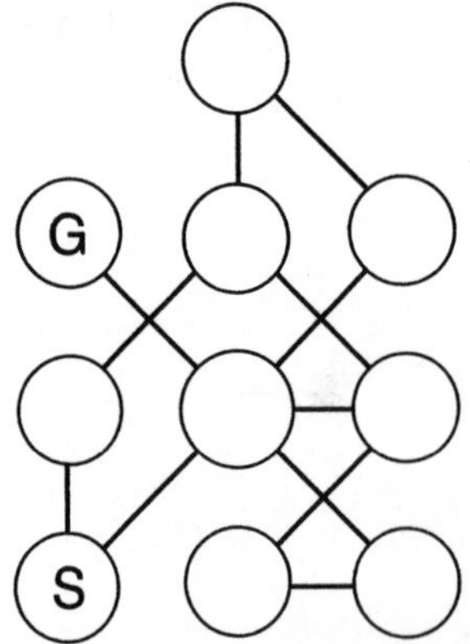

GOLDEN SOMBRERO

Answers on pages 183–184.

Ballpark Lingo

LANGUAGE

Can you unscramble these anagrams to come up with terms often heard in major league ball? We've added clues to help.

1. OTHER HONDURAN: Double play going from third base to second to first.

2. OUTGOING CHALK: When a batter is called out on strikes.

3. METAL LAB: Easy pitch to hit.

4. REGULATE AXES: Bloop hit that drops between an infielder and outfielder.

Utility Man

CREATIVE THINKING | SPATIAL VISUALIZATION | VISUAL LOGIC

Draw lines to like utilities (water to water, gas to gas, electricity to electricity, telephone to telephone) without any line crossing another line.

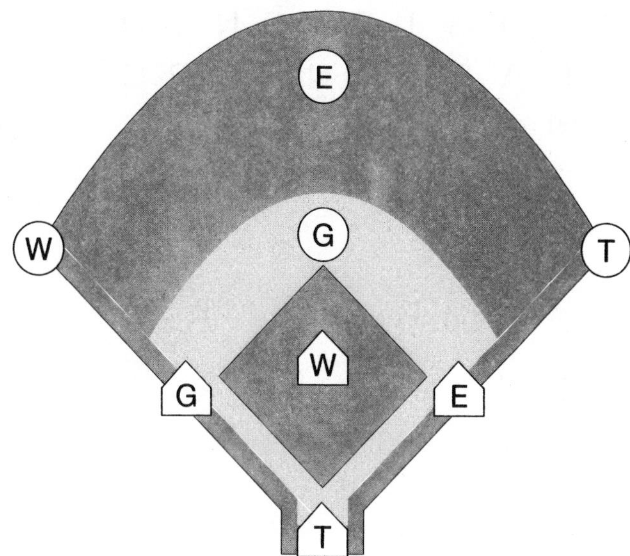

Answers on page 184.

Sluggers

ATTENTION | VISUAL SEARCH

Every Hall of Fame infielder listed below and on the next page is contained within the group of letters. Names can be found in a straight line horizontally, vertically, or diagonally. They may be read either forward or backward. When complete, the left-over letters will spell a quote from Vin Scully.

```
L O W N O S N I B O R S I N F
G C E P E D A F T R A Y N O R
H O R N S B Y U R E E S E S I
E Y B R E W Z F G L S T W I S
O E E M A Z E R O S K I T S C
R V L R I P E H S X E U T L H
E O L R H E A A T A P A N E K
K C I W N P N R C A R E W R E
N C K B P S E Z I M M R R R L
I M E L O N K S I C N D N E L
T R I N G I P N G N I U G O Z
G N F A E E I N A G R O M D L
G S W G E H R I G B O B G O O
D T D I M H C S A N D B E R G
```

ANSON	BOUDREAU	DOERR	GREENBERG
APARICIO	BRETT	EVERS	HORNSBY
APPLING	CAREW	FOX	KILLEBREW
BANKS	CEPEDA	FRISCH	MATHEWS
BOGGS	CHANCE	GEHRIG	MAZEROSKI

Answers on page 184.

MCCOVEY	REESE	SANDBERG	TRAYNOR
MIZE	RIPKEN	SCHMIDT	WAGNER
MORGAN	RIZZUTO	SISLER	
PEREZ	ROBINSON	TINKER	

Leftover letters: ______________________________

Word Columns

LANGUAGE PLANNING

Find the hidden humorous pun by using the letters directly below each of the blank squares. Each letter is used only once. A black square indicates the end of a word.

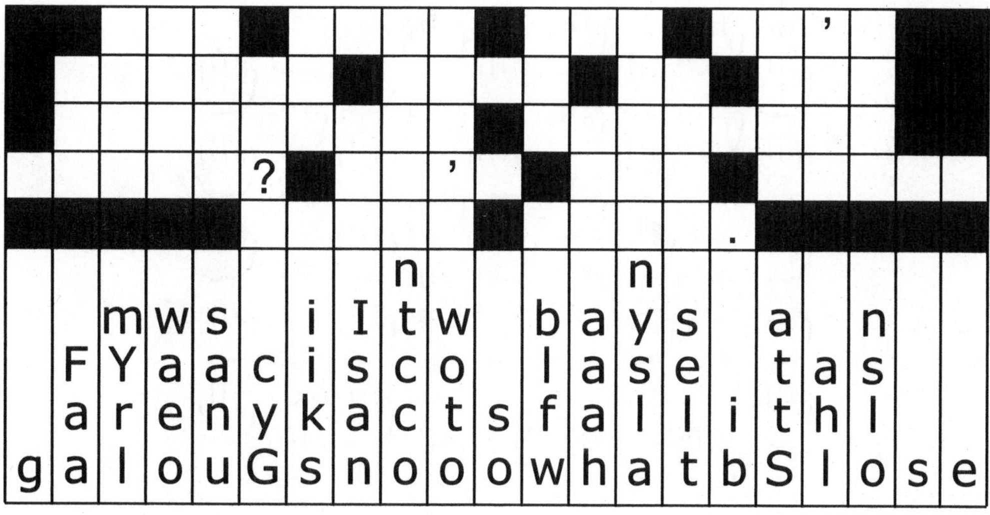

Answers on page 184.

Anagram Heroes

LANGUAGE

Below are anagrams of 4 famous sports figures. Which one is NOT an anagram for a Yankees great?

1. CAMEL MET INKY

2. ED JEER TREK

3. JEAN MOAT ON

4. EDIFY WORTH

Hidden Ball Trick

ANALYSIS PLANNING

Locate balls hidden in these gloves. Each arrow points to only one ball in that row, and each ball is pointed to by only one arrow. Balls are not found in neighboring gloves.

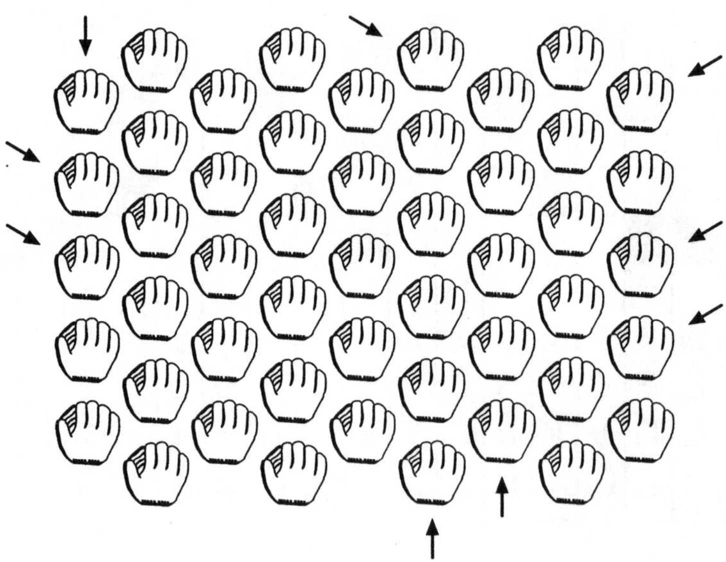

Answers on page 184.

Mix n' Match

GENERAL KNOWLEDGE

Match the team to its mascot.

Team			Mascot
Pittsburgh	☐	☐	Mr. Redlegs
Arizona	☐	☐	D. Baxter the Bobcat
Seattle	☐	☐	Raymond
Cincinnati	☐	☐	Captain Jolly Roger
Detroit	☐	☐	Wally the Green Monster
Philadelphia	☐	☐	Swinging Friar
Tampa Bay	☐	☐	Phanatic
San Diego	☐	☐	Mariner Moose
Boston	☐	☐	Paws

Unforgettable Teams? (Part I)

MEMORY

Study these team names for one minute. When you're done, turn the page for a memory challenge.

ASTROS   *Phillies*

Braves   GIANTS

REDS   *Tigers*

METS   *Dodgers*

RED SOX   *MARINERS*

Answers on page 184.

Unforgettable Teams? (Part II)

MEMORY

(Do not read this until you've read the previous page.)

Using your memory, circle the teams that were listed on the previous page.

Braves	Red Sox	Dodgers	Astros
Brewers	Reds	Phillies	Mets
Cubs	Orioles	Indians	Cardinals

Codeword

ANALYSIS LANGUAGE

2	16	16	12	1	22	26		17	19	25	7	24
17		19		26		14		26		19		20
26	19	17	19	4	6	26		24	19	11	7	16
26		26		21		18		26		9		17
20	3	12	2	26		5	16	7	9	3	4	21
				7		7				17		26
5	11	25	16	7	24		9	16	10	26	9	9
26		19				9		21				
12	3	17	19	1	9	26		19	24	24	19	22
17		11		16		24		13		23		11
16	17	7	11	8		7	17	11	1	3	7	26
11		26		16		26		18		19		9
19	20	21	6	24		17	26	19	4	7	26	12

A B C D E F G H I J K L M N O P Q R S T U V W X Y Z

1	2	3	4	5	6	7	8	9	10	11	12	13
						T						

14	15	16	17	18	19	20	21	22	23	24	25	26
			R							S		

The letters of the alphabet are hidden in code: They are represented by a number from 1 through 26. With the letters already given, complete the crossword puzzle and break the code. When you do, you'll discover the last names of 9 players who were on the 2009 Boston Red Sox roster.

Answers on page 184.

Yer Out!

PLANNING | SPATIAL REASONING

Beginning at the bottom, can you guide the path of the ball to the fielder's mitt?

Trivia on the Brain

Nolan Ryan had the longest career in major league baseball. He entered the majors in 1966 and played on 4 different teams before hanging up his spikes in 1993, playing 27 seasons.

Answer on page 185.

Triple Crown

GENERAL KNOWLEDGE LANGUAGE

ACROSS

1. Copier paper purchase
5. Bikini part
8. _____ Gehrig, Triple Crown winner in 1934
11. Minimal effort
12. Has a bug
14. Clip-_____ (some bow ties)
15. Triple Crown winner in 1966
18. Like yarns or webs
19. Source of poi
20. Feeling of rage
22. Toil away
26. "Eureka!"
29. Way out there
30. Like the Sahara
31. With 33-Across, Triple Crown winner in 1956
33. See 31-Across
35. Ms. Brockovich
36. _____ Paese cheese
37. _____ Francisco (NL city since 1958)
38. Roomy auto
40. Bug in a hobby farm
41. Maker of the first all-rubber basketball
43. Home to most of Turkey

47. Triple Crown winner in 1922 and 1925
52. Santa _____ winds
53. Inheritors of the Earth, in the Bible
54. _____ podrida (spicy stew)
55. _____ Williams, Triple Crown winner in 1942 and 1947
56. Magazine staffers: abbr.
57. "This _____ in Baseball" (FOX show)

DOWN

1. Ring official, for short
2. "Rabbit _____" (ballplayer's oversensitivity to razzing)
3. "Quickly!" on a memo
4. Waiter's handout
5. "Cheers" setting
6. One causing civil unrest
7. Jessica of "Sin City"
8. _____ Angeles (NL city since 1958)
9. Beatle bride Yoko _____
10. Adm.'s service branch
13. Knighted ones
16. Bowie's weapon
17. Ryan, who tossed seven no-hitters
21. Tampa Bay player
23. Liberal _____
24. "This Old House" host Bob
25. Biblical garden
26. Iowa State's city
27. Add to the staff
28. Etcher's fluid
32. Unprincipled sort
33. "Eight _____ Out" (1988 baseball movie)
34. Place to exchange vows
36. Soaked in the tub
39. 1961 AL batting champ _____ Cash
42. Fortune-teller's words
44. Cleveland's 2007 home opener was called on account of this
45. Elba, Napoleon's place of exile, is one
46. "_____ was I ere I saw Elba"
47. Lab maze runner
48. Retired number worn by Ozzie Smith and Pee Wee Reese
49. _____ about (wander)
50. Gives approval to
51. Shaggy Tibetan beast

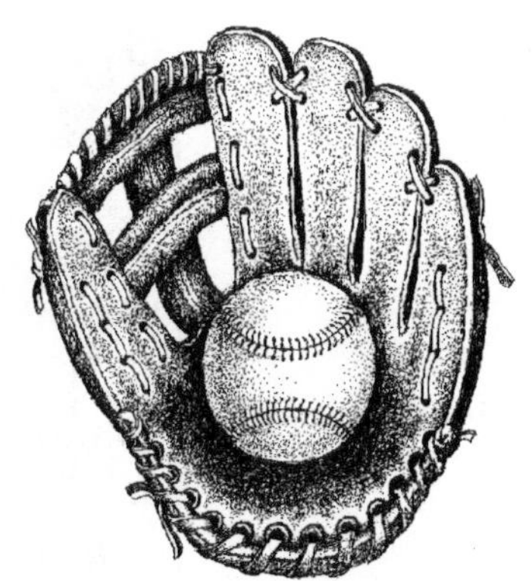

Answers on page 185.

You Heard It Here First

LANGUAGE LOGIC

Cryptograms are messages in substitution code. Break the code to read the quote and its source. For example, THE SMART CAT might become FVO QWGDF JGF if **F** is substituted for **T, V** for **H, O** for **E,** and so on.

"Q'B YFXYRZ ANYOB QM LJWFBU'M KN BJUN, KWM ZJDNMQDNZ QM BJU'M YFXYRZ XJOH."

—AYFF JT TYDN DYUYCNO LYZNR ZMNUCNF

Missing Connections

LANGUAGE PLANNING

It's a crossword without the clues! Use the letters below to fill in the empty spaces in the crossword grid. When you are finished, you'll have words that read both across and down, crossword-style.

E E E F L M M N N O R S S T W X X Y Z

Answers on page 185.

Fireballer

CREATIVE THINKING | SPATIAL VISUALIZATION | VISUAL LOGIC

How many baseballs are depicted in the arrangement below?

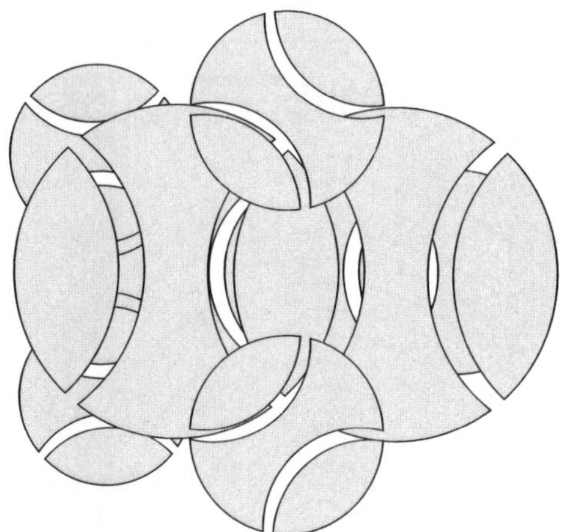

Play Ball!

LANGUAGE

Fill in the blanks in each sentence below with 5-letter words that are anagrams (rearrangements of the same letters) of one another.

1. A pitcher's _______ is based on how well he can _______.
2. The sports writer _______ all the players involved in the recent _______.
3. The potential base-stealer who _______ when taking a lead will need more than a well-executed _______ if he hopes to succeed.
4. A fast baserunner may _______ at _______ one base per game.
5. The baserunner barely mussed a _______ in his uniform when he slid into home _____.

Answers on page 185.

It's Outta Here!

PLANNING SPATIAL REASONING

Can you follow the slugger's blast to the ball's location in the center of the maze?

Trivia on the Brain

Whose baseball card is the most valuable to date? Babe Ruth's? Willie Mays's? Actually, it's Honus Wagner's, whose T206 baseball card—originally released in 1909—sold for $2.35 million in 2007!

Answer on page 185.

Lineup Card

GENERAL KNOWLEDGE

Fill in the blanks to spell out great players associated with a particular team. Every occurrence of every letter of that team's name has been filled in. As a bonus, can you name the team?

1. L __ __   __ r __ __ __
2. D i __ __ __   D __ a __
3. __ __ __   __ i __ s __ n
4. S __ a n   __ __ s i a l
5. __ n __ s   S l a __ __ __ __ __ r
6. __ __ __ i __   S __ i __ __
7. R __ __ __ r s   __ __ r n s __ __
8. __ r __ c __   S __ __ __ __ __

Team: ________________

Network

ANALYSIS   LOGIC

Place letters into the empty circles so that the given words can be spelled out in order from letter to consecutive letter through connected circles. Letters can be used more than once, and you can double back to the same letter.

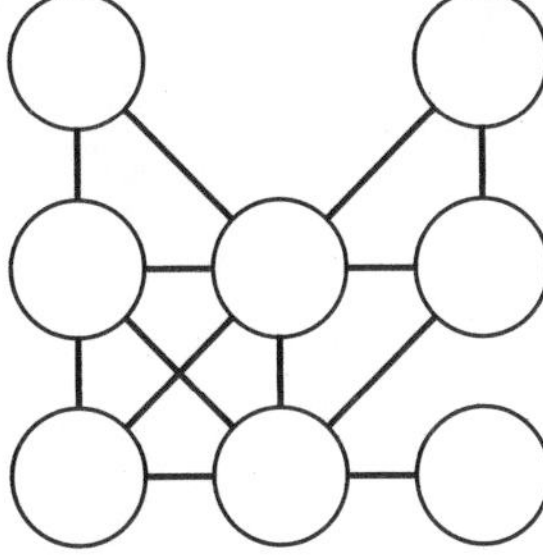

DISABLED LIST

Answers on page 185.

DRIVING IT HOME

LEVEL 5

Picture This

SPATIAL REASONING

VISUAL LOGIC

Place each of the 18 boxes in the 5 by 5 grid so they form a picture of items used in the game of baseball. Do this without cutting the page apart: Use only your eyes. Seven boxes will remain blank.

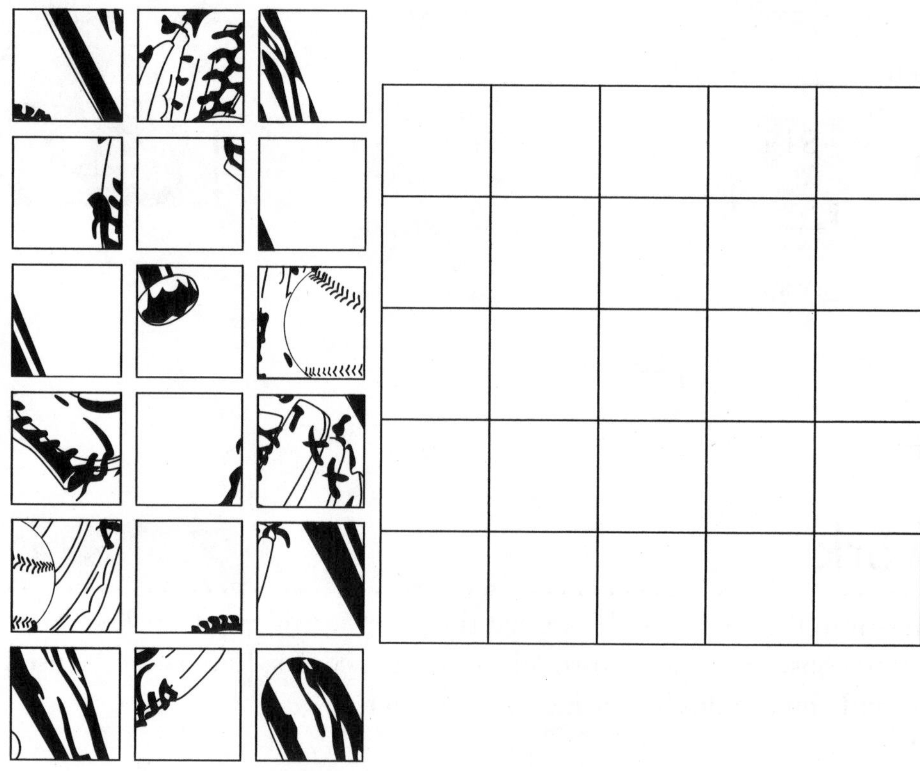

Answer on page 185.

Rhyme Time

GENERAL KNOWLEDGE LANGUAGE

Each clue leads to a 2-word answer that rhymes, such as BIG PIG or STABLE TABLE. The numbers in parentheses after the clue give the number of letters in each word of the answer. For example, "cookware taken from the oven (3, 3)" would be "hot pot."

1. Cincinnati's manager (4, 3): ________________
2. Rickey Henderson's status among base-stealers (5, 5): ________________
3. A four-run homer under false pretenses (4, 4): ________________
4. Less than an inning of work from the bullpen (5, 6): ________________
5. Tissues used by Brewers' ace Zack: (8, 7): ________________
6. Imperiled player in Arlington (6, 6): ________________
7. A third-base coach's instruction (5, 5): ________________
8. A squad's strategy (4, 6): ________________
9. Where you might find Clemens's keys, wallet, etc. (7, 7): ________________
10. A hot streak at the plate (3, 3): ________________
11. A rundown, in other words (4, 5): ________________
12. An error in baseball needlework (6, 6): ________________
13. A conversation about bases on balls (4, 4): ________________
14. An MVP's surgical souvenirs (5, 5): ________________
15. A fear of fielding foul-ups (5, 6): ________________
16. Problems with two-baggers (6, 7): ________________

Answers on page 186.

Working Title

ANALYSIS LOGIC

Can you identify the correct titles of these baseball movies from the overwrought titles listed on the marquee?

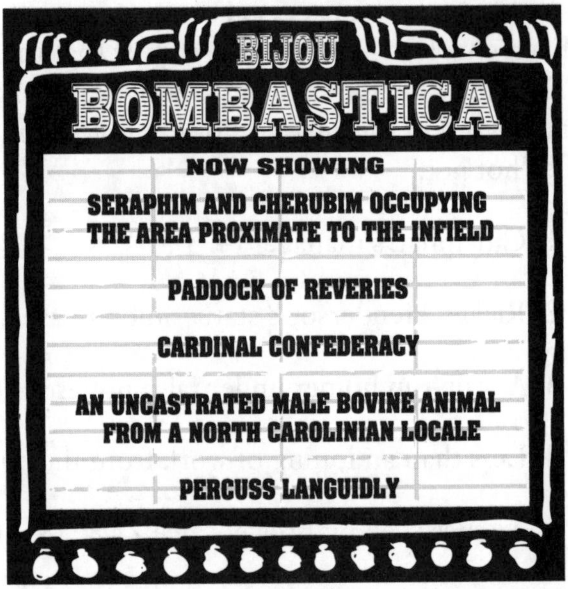

Point Counterpoint

CREATIVE THINKING SPATIAL VISUALIZATION VISUAL LOGIC

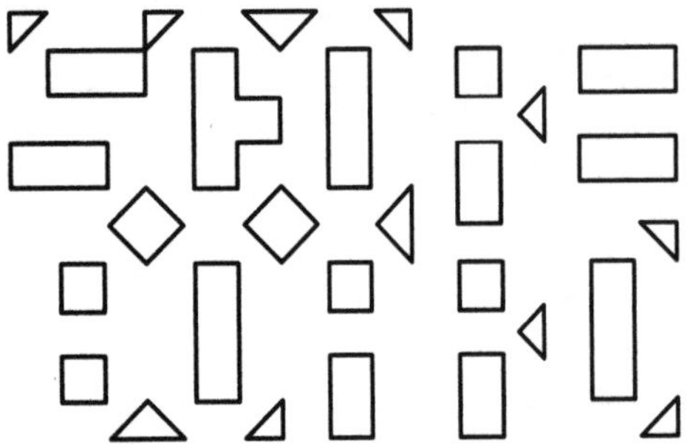

This mishmash of shapes to the left appears meaningless. However, if you superimpose the blank grid directly on top of the shapes, you will see that the shapes spell a word. If you can't do this using only your eyes, trace the grid on a piece of thin paper, then place it over the group of shapes.

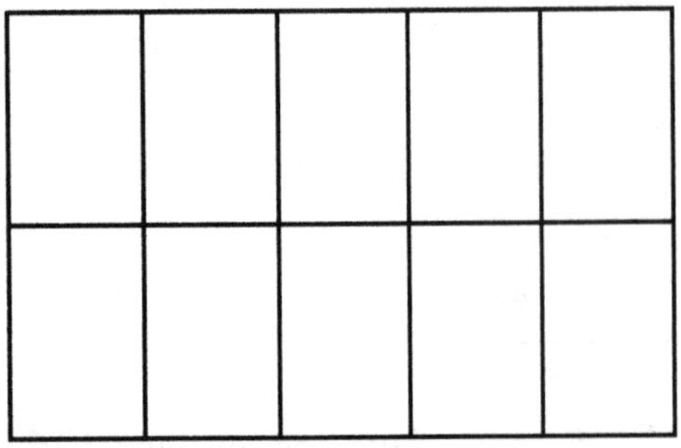

Answers on page 186.

Lineup Card

GENERAL KNOWLEDGE

Fill in the blanks to spell out great players associated with a particular team. Every occurrence of every letter of that team's name has been filled in. As a bonus, can you name the team?

1. ___ a ___ e   ___ ___ r ___ ___ ___

2. ___ ___ ___ ___   ___ ___ e ___ r ___

3. ___ a ___ ___   A a r ___ ___

4. ___ a r r e ___   S ___ a ___ ___

5. E ___ ___ ___ e   ___ ___ ___ ___ e ___ s

6. A ___ ___ r ___ ___   ___ ___ ___ e s

7. ___ ___ ___ ___ ___ e r   ___ ___ ___ e s

8. ___ ___ ___   ___ ___ a v ___ ___ e

9. ___ r e ___   ___ a ___ ___ ___ ___

Team: ____________________

Trivia on the Brain

A common "unwritten rule" in baseball is to not talk about a "no-hitter" while it's in progress. Otherwise, you'll jinx it. This applies to players, announcers, and fans alike.

Answers on page 186.

Word Search

ATTENTION | VISUAL SEARCH

Every slugger listed in the right column and on the next page is contained within the group of letters below. Names can be found in a straight line horizontally, vertically, or diagonally. They may be read either forward or backward. Leftover letters spell a quote from Hall of Fame manager Casey Stengel.

```
I W A S M S U C E H A D A J N
G M S T A R G E L L E R O A U
S C Y S R K H N L I T R T C C
K G E A I K S W E Z S U L K O
N W R N S C I E B L V T L S L
A I E E H T W N G A L H L O A
B R O M C G R I F F A A E N V
T E I R M R I Z L Y I R W N I
T D N I A E N E E S A M O H T
T L Z C T E N A U M O R P N O
W E T E H N I M M O S N R N A
K I L L E B R E W G D K L U O
W F N A W E D E I S N L I C M
K O O F S R L R D S O I E D U
U X S S I G H T A I B S K R R
I X W Y T E N G N W N B A A P
T T A A G E L I N A O S G P H
R A D M C T R D C I M H C E Y
```

AARON
ALLEN
BANKS
BELLE
BENCH
BONDS
CANSECO
COLAVITO
DAWSON
FIELDER
FOSTER
FOXX
GEHRIG
GREENBERG

Answers on page 186.

HOWARD	MARIS	MURRAY	SOSA
JACKSON	MATHEWS	MUSIAL	STARGELL
KILLEBREW	MAYS	POWELL	THOMAS
KINER	MCGRIFF	RICE	WILSON
KINGMAN	MCGWIRE	RUTH	WINFIELD
KLUSZEWSKI	MIZE	SCHMIDT	YASTRZEMSKI
MANTLE	MURPHY	SNIDER	

Leftover letters: ______________________________

____

Play Ball!

LANGUAGE

Fill in the blanks in each sentence below with 6-letter words that are anagrams (rearrangements of the same letters) of one another.

1. The _______ of the rumor is of _______ a disgruntled former teammate.

2. _______ razzing from fans _______ when playing at home.

3. Our best reliever came on to ______ his teammates and was able to ______ a win.

4. The fielder in _______ is a _______ acquisition from a rival team.

5. An _______ can be forgiven for having an _______ thought once in a while.

6. It was obvious in the slow-motion _______ which _______ started the fight.

Answers on page 186.

Double Jumble

LANGUAGE

It's 2 jumbles in 1! First, unscramble the 7 letters under each row of squares to form common English words and write the words in the boxes. When you've completed the first jumble, unscramble the letters running down each column (in the dark boxes) to reveal 2 baseball-related words.

S E L A S W L

O O D C A A V

J E T D E C E

V E D E B O L

M A I M O A N

S L O M B O S

I N S O A L I

I S T U L I M

Answers on page 186.

Swing Batter!

PLANNING | SPATIAL REASONING

Can you follow the ball as it curves its way toward the batter's swing?

Trivia on the Brain

Once upon a time, players could be fined for giving away baseballs. But these days public relations are of so much importance that no one says a word when a ball goes "missing."

Answer on page 186.

Hidden Ball Trick

ANALYSIS PLANNING

Locate balls hidden in these gloves. Each arrow points to only one ball in that row, and each ball is pointed to by only one arrow. Balls are not found in neighboring gloves.

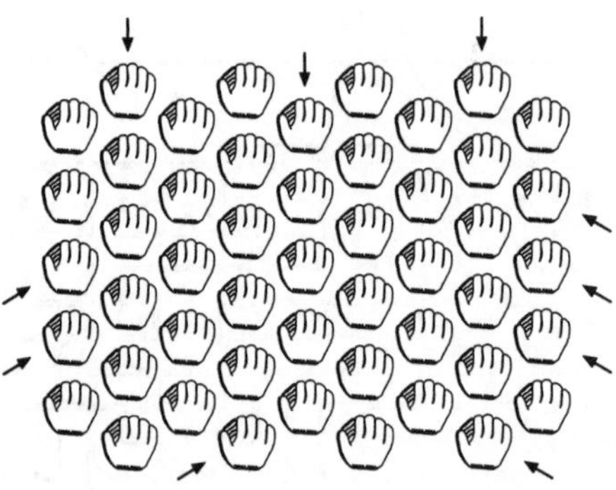

Word Ladder

LANGUAGE PLANNING

Using the clues along the way, change just one letter on each line to go from the top word to the bottom word. Do not change the order of the letters. You must have a common English word at each step.

PLAY

____

____

_______ unruly child

____

_______ keeps your pants up

____

BALL

Answers on page 187.

Missing Connections

LANGUAGE PLANNING

It's a crossword without the clues! Use the letters below to fill in the empty spaces in the crossword grid. When you are finished, you'll have words that read both across and down, crossword-style.

A A A A A C C E E E E E G H J L L N N O R R S S S S V V Z

Utility Man

CREATIVE THINKING SPATIAL VISUALIZATION VISUAL LOGIC

Draw lines to like utilities (water to water, gas to gas, electricity to electricity, telephone to telephone) without any line crossing another line.

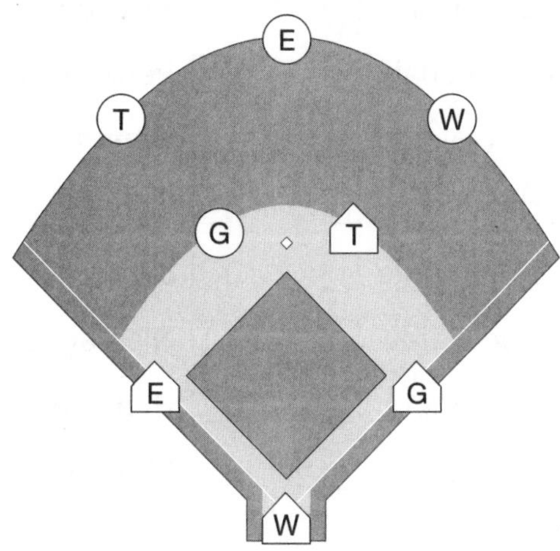

Answers on page 187.

Chalk Talk

ANALYSIS LOGIC

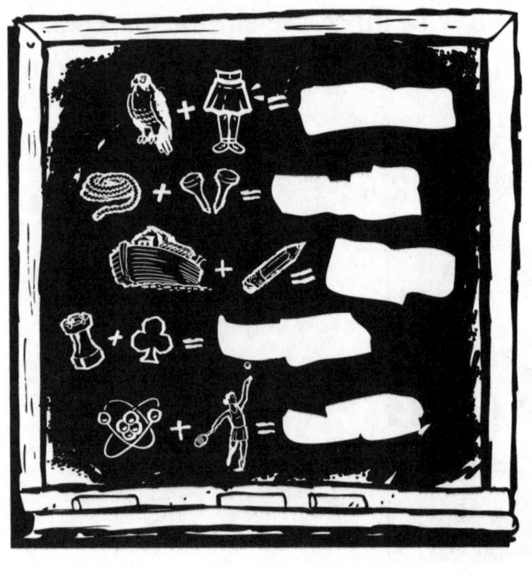

Can you identify these 5 baseball greats by solving these anagram equations? Identify the images, then rearrange the letters to discover each name. For example, ALARM + MALL + NET would equal Alan Trammell.

Mix n' Match

GENERAL KNOWLEDGE

Can you match the All-Star to his place of birth?

Bert Blyleven ☐	☐ Dominican Republic
Dennis Martinez ☐	☐ Netherlands
Ferguson Jenkins ☐	☐ Puerto Rico
Fernando Valenzuela ☐	☐ Venezuela
Hideo Nomo ☐	☐ Canada
Omar Vizquel ☐	☐ Cuba
Roberto Clemente ☐	☐ Japan
Rod Carew ☐	☐ Nicaragua
Rafael Palmeiro ☐	☐ Panama
Vladimir Guerrero ☐	☐ Mexico

Answers on page 187.

Double Jumble

LANGUAGE

It's 2 jumbles in 1! First, unscramble the 7 letters under each row of squares to form common English words and write the words in the boxes. When you've completed the first jumble, unscramble the letters running down each column (in the dark boxes) to reveal 2 baseball-related words.

F L H W T T E

S C E I P N T

I R T S I A C

X U S I O N A

M E G S L I P

S P N O O T N

I A R R T O

I R A L V I O

Answers on page 187.

Lineup Card

GENERAL KNOWLEDGE

Fill in the blanks to spell out great players or managers associated with a particular team. Every occurrence of every letter of that team's name has been filled in. As a bonus, can you name the team?

1.___ ___ s e ___ S t e ___ ___ e ___

2. ___ ___ ___ ___ ___ ___ ___ e s

3. T ___ m S e ___ ___ e ___

4. ___ ___ s t ___ S t ___ ___ ___

5. ___ ___ ___ ___ ___ ___ ___ S t ___ ___ ___ ___ e ___ ___ ___

6. ___ ___ ___ ___ ___ t ___ ___ ___ ___ e ___

Team: ____________________

Curveball

ANALYSIS LOGIC

Starting from each number outside the grid, draw a line leading from that number to a mitt. No lines can intersect, and the number of boxes the line must pass through coincides with the number it originates from. So, if a line starts at the number 6, it must pass through 6 boxes (including the box the mitt is in). All boxes will be used.

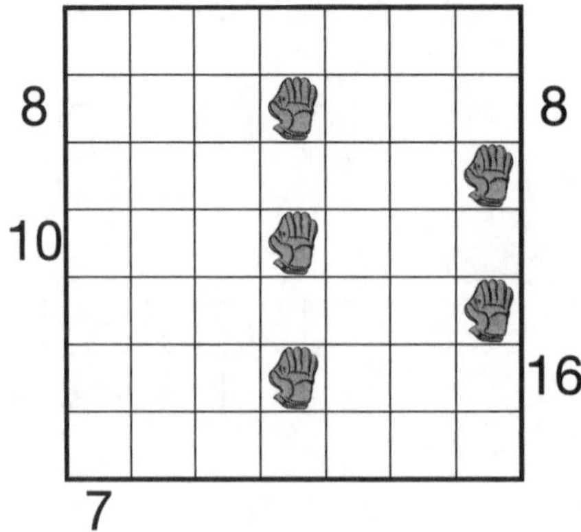

Answers on pages 187–188.

Word Columns

LANGUAGE PLANNING

Find the hidden quote from Sparky Anderson by using the letters directly below each of the blank squares. Each letter is used only once. A black square indicates the end of a word unless the word ends at the end of a row.

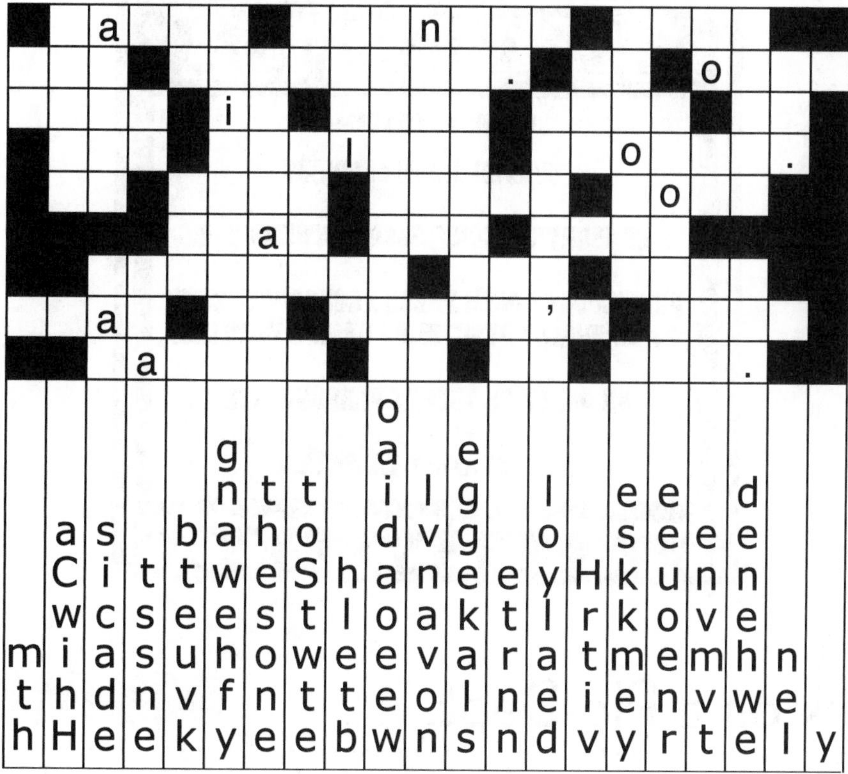

Answer on page 188.

Working Title

ANALYSIS LOGIC

Can you identify the correct titles of these baseball movies from the overwrought titles listed on the marquee?

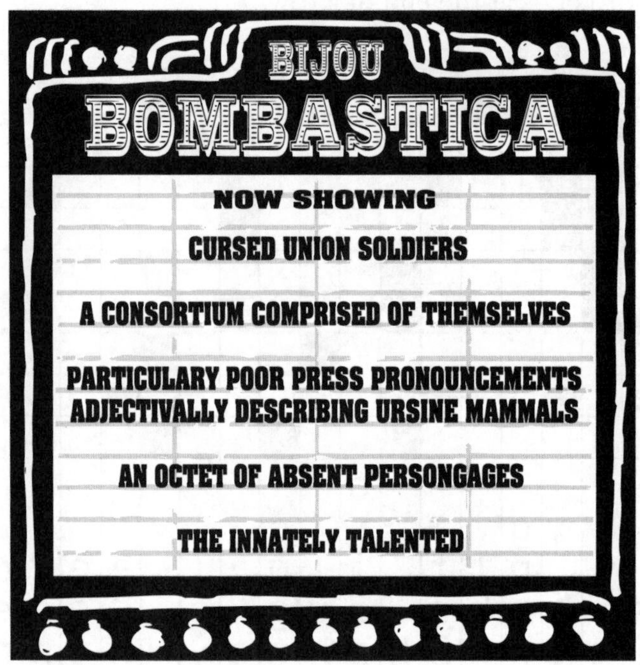

BIJOU
BOMBASTICA
NOW SHOWING
CURSED UNION SOLDIERS
A CONSORTIUM COMPRISED OF THEMSELVES
PARTICULARY POOR PRESS PRONOUNCEMENTS
ADJECTIVALLY DESCRIBING URSINE MAMMALS
AN OCTET OF ABSENT PERSONGAGES
THE INNATELY TALENTED

Lipstick on a Pig Dept.

LANGUAGE LOGIC

Cryptograms are messages in substitution code. Break the code to read the humorous quote and its source. For example, THE SMART CAT might become FVO QWGDF JGF if **F** is substituted for **T, V** for **H, O** for **E,** and so on.

"WM GFTTRPZE F ATPMCGFJM PJ DPYM F SQI VQE NMFTPZE MFTTPZEJ."

—JXFTYR FZVMTJQZ

Answers on page 188.

Baseball Basics (Part I)

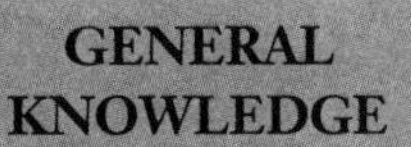

MEMORY

Take this quiz, check your answers on page 188, then turn the page for a memory test on what you've learned.

1. The difference between a baseball glove and a baseball mitt is:
   (a) Gloves have fingers, mitts don't.
   (b) Mitts have fingers, gloves don't.
   (c) No difference, they're the same thing.
   (d) Only the catcher is allowed to use a mitt; all the others use gloves.

2. What two things are a fielder not allowed to use to catch a ball?

3. With a runner on third, the batter bunts in hopes that the runner will score. This is called a _____ play.

4. In baseball's scoring system, the letter K stands for:
   (a) a foul
   (b) a strikeout
   (c) a walk
   (d) a kiss shot

5. How many umpires are on the field in a World Series game?
   (a) 4
   (b) 5
   (c) 6
   (d) 7

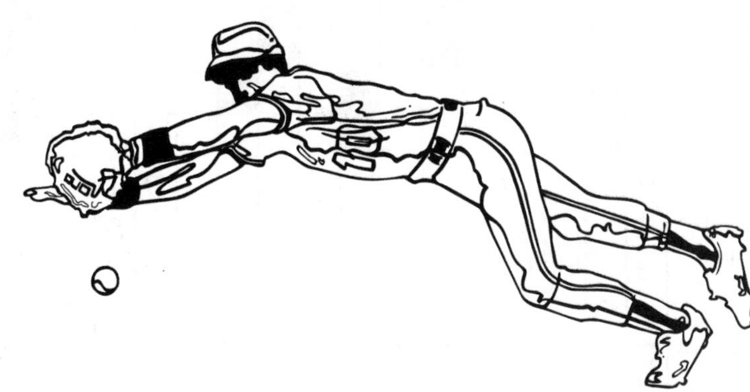

Answers on page 188.

Baseball Basics (Part II)

MEMORY

(Do not read this until you've taken the quiz on the previous page.)

Based on the information from the previous page, can you answer these five true or false questions?

1. A fielder can't use his cap to catch a ball except in the ninth inning.

2. A squeeze play is when a runner is caught between second and third base.

3. In scoring, a strikeout is indicated by a K.

4. There are 5 umpires on the field in a World Series game.

5. Only the catcher and third baseman are allowed to use mitts.

Word Columns

LANGUAGE PLANNING

Find the hidden quote from Tommy Lasorda by using the letters directly below each of the blank squares. Each letter is used only once. A black square indicates the end of a word.

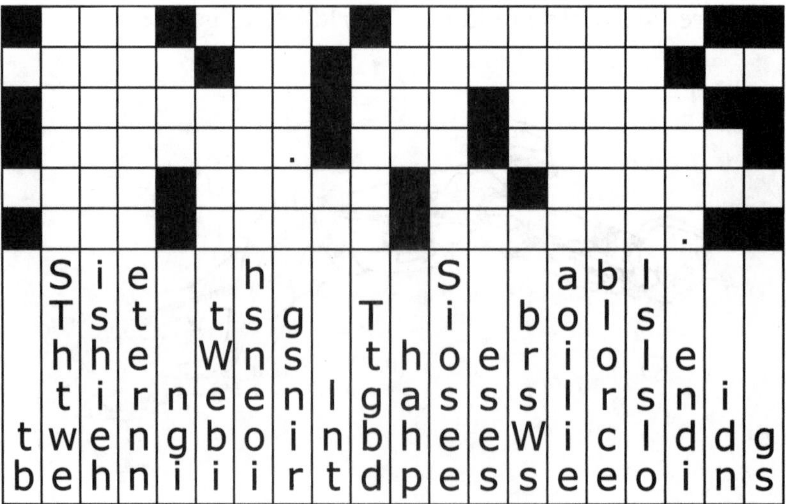

Answers on page 188.

Double Jumble

LANGUAGE

It's 2 jumbles in 1! First, unscramble the 7 letters under each row of squares to form common English words and write the words in the boxes. When you've completed the first jumble, unscramble the letters running down each column (in the dark boxes) to reveal 2 baseball-related words.

O T A S U F U

E I T N N E L

S T E R A B A

F R O I C E F

O U L R A F M

B I R D S U T

H E E C R A A

Trivia on the Brain

Before he was president, Ronald Reagan was an actor. In 1952, he portrayed Grover Cleveland Alexander in *The Winning Team.*

Answers on page 188.

Chalk Talk

ANALYSIS LOGIC

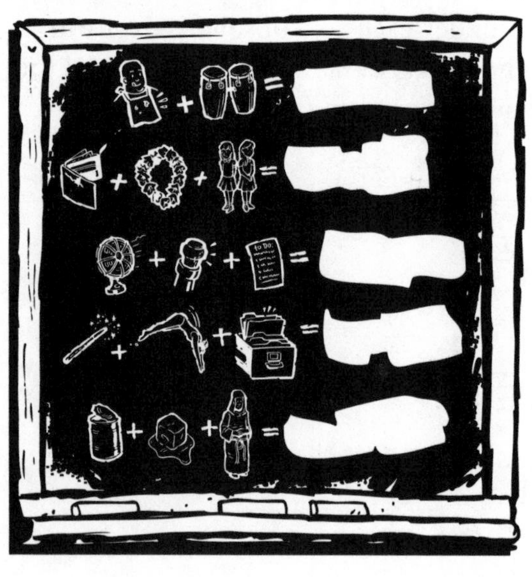

Can you identify these 5 Hall of Famers by solving these anagram equations. Identify the images, then rearrange the letters to discover each name. For example, ALARM + MALL + NET would equal Alan Trammell.

Network

ANALYSIS LOGIC

Place letters into the empty circles so that the given words can be spelled out in order from letter to consecutive letter through connected circles. Letters can be used more than once, and you can double back to the same letter.

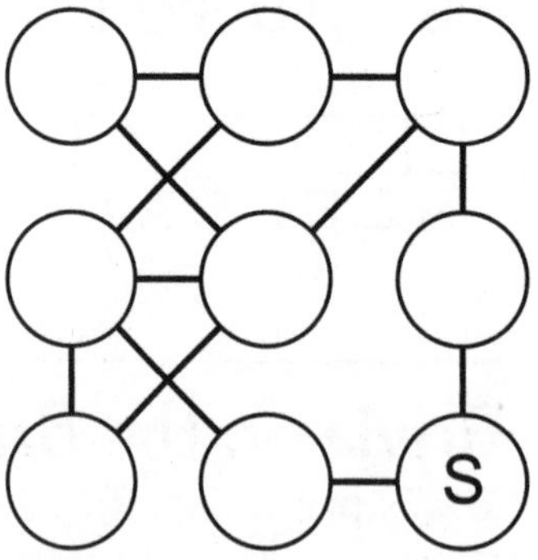

INFIELD SHIFT

Answers on page 188.

College Baseball by Alpha Sleuth™

LANGUAGE PLANNING

Move each of the letters below into the grid to form common words. You will use each letter once. The letters in the numbered cells of the grid correspond to the letters in the phrase at the bottom. Completing the grid will help you complete the phrase and vice versa. When finished, the grid and phrase should be filled with valid words, and you will have used all the letters in the letter set.

Hint: The numbered cells in the grid are arranged alphabetically, so the letter in the cell marked 1 will appear in the alphabet before the letter in the cell marked 2, and so on.

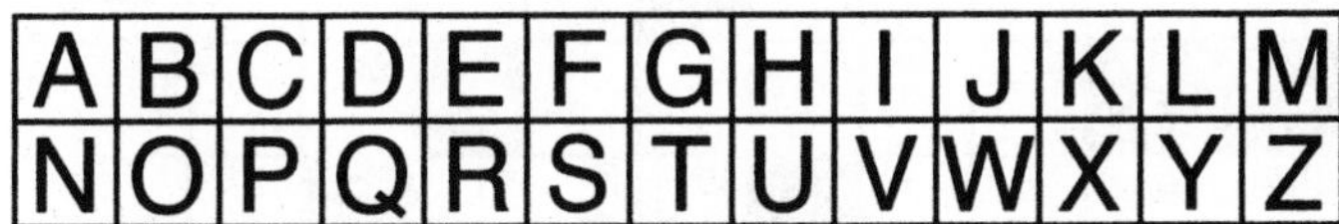

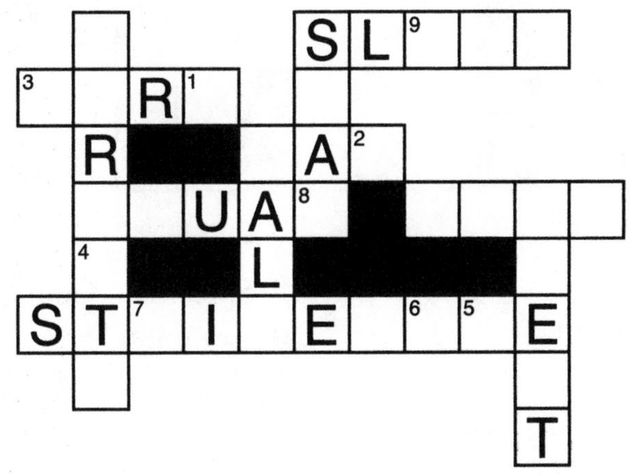

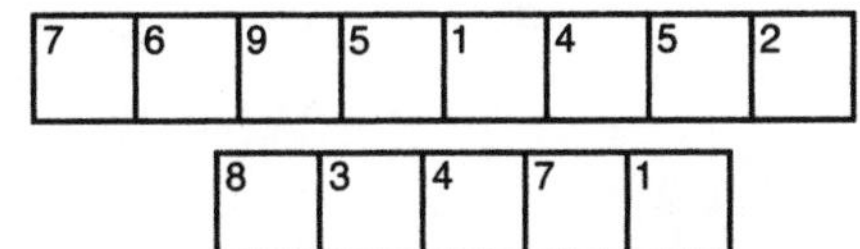

Answers on page 189.

Home Games

GENERAL KNOWLEDGE | LANGUAGE

1	2	3	4	5	■	6	7	8	■	9	10	11
12					■	13			■	14		
15					16				■	17		
■	■	18						■	19			
20	21		■	22			■	23				
24			25	■	26		27			■	■	■
28				29		■	30			31	32	33
■	■	■	34			35		■	36			
37	38	39			■	40		41	■	42		
43				■	44				45		■	■
46			■	47							48	49
50			■	51			■	52				
53			■	54			■	55				

ACROSS

1. Marking on a baseball bat
6. Dennis the Menace, e.g.
9. Bit of video gear attached to a catcher's helmet, perhaps
12. Where Bowie fell
13. Whisper sweet nothings
14. "To a..." poem
15. Home of the Mets
17. Mantric words
18. Dazed state
19. Speaker in Cooperstown
20. Common happy hour day: abbr.
22. Dam-building org.
23. 1959 Johnny Mathis hit
24. "Hit 'em where they _____": Wee Willie Keeler
26. Big name in printers
28. With 30-Across, home of the Blue Jays
30. See 28-Across
34. Words of denial

36. Time period for many baseball records
37. Ex post _____
40. "SNL" alum _____ Gasteyer
42. Merino mama
43. Calls from the bleachers
44. Cockney, e.g.
46. "… man _____ mouse?"
47. Home of the Padres
50. Precursor of Microsoft Windows
51. 2008 World Series player
52. Myopic Mr. voiced by Jim Backus
53. Number of fingers in a catcher's fastball signal, classically
54. Drop an easy pop fly, say
55. Vehicles with runners

DOWN

1. Fond du _____, Wisconsin
2. "Thrilla in Manila" victor
3. Cobb led the league in it 12 times
4. Mideast ruler
5. Dietetic, on food labels
6. Polar topper
7. Suburban lawn ruiner
8. Cacao plant feature
9. _____ Field (home of the Rockies)
10. Word on a ticket
11. Like Oscar Madison
16. Follow a broker's advice, perhaps
19. Cheap-sounding
20. Word before fetched or flung
21. Brazilian hot spot
23. WWII spy and former major leaguer _____ Berg
25. Outdoor party setups
27. Like an overlook view
29. Aussie bounder
31. Like some former ML "bonus babies," upon callup
32. Like an inexperienced rookie
33. Bard's before
35. Joan of Arc, for one
37. Tolkien's ring-bearer
38. Homer king before Bonds
39. _____ Field (home of the Diamondbacks)
41. Elemental units
44. "Bad News" ballplayer of film
45. Birthstone for many Libras
47. Lead-in for law or med
48. Carew, seven-time AL leader in 3-Down
49. Many bout endings for 2-Down: abbr.

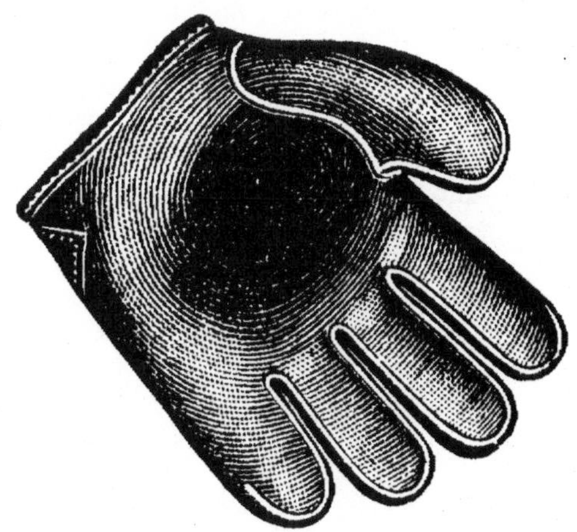

Answers on page 189.

Picture This

SPATIAL REASONING | VISUAL LOGIC

Place each of the 20 boxes in the 5 by 4 grid on the left so they form a picture of favorite baseball snacks. Do this without cutting the page apart: Use only your eyes.

Word Ladder

LANGUAGE | PLANNING

Change just one letter on each line to go from the top word to the bottom word. Do not change the order of the letters. You must have a common English word at each step.

AWAY

______

______

______

______

______

______

______

GAME

Answers on page 189.

Rhyme Time

GENERAL KNOWLEDGE · LANGUAGE

Each clue leads to a 2- or 3-word answer that rhymes, such as BIG PIG or STABLE TABLE. The numbers in parentheses after the clue give the number of letters in each word of the answer. For example, "cookware taken from the oven (3, 3)" would be "hot pot."

1. Second baseman Nellie who played in the '59 World Series (3, 3): ____________
2. Discussion about umps' call against a pitcher (4, 4): ________________
3. A decision about the San Diego team following its sale (6, 4): ______________
4. A part of Giants' history (4, 3 4): ____________
5. A charged assessed for hitting them out right down the line (4 4, 4): _________
6. How he determined the length of his lead-offs, when to start his slides, etc. (4 4, 4): _____________
7. The right way he got under the tag to score the winning run (4 4, 5): _________
8. When they brought in the relief pitcher who was completely off his game, the... (4 4, 5): _____________
9. He had such complete control over the big-screen display system that they called him the... (10, 4): _____________
10. Something that didn't occur when mighty Casey struck out (8, 6): ____________
11. Boston headline after Ortiz hit a walk-off grand slam (3 5, 5): ______________
12. The reason they were able to select great young players year after year (5 4, 5): ______________
13. When the star refused to sign his name for the boy he later learned was the owner's son (9, 5): _______________

Answers on page 189.

ANSWERS

Grid Fill (page 9)

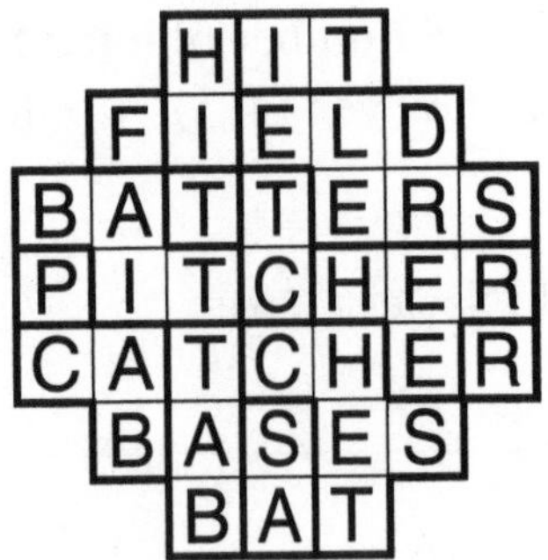

Word Jigsaw (page 9)

Pic-a-Pix (page 10)

Word Ladder (page 11)

Answers may vary.
BALL, gall/bale, gale, GAME

Name Calling (page 11)

"Hit 'em where they ain't."

The Shading Game (page 12)

4	5	1	9	8	2	4	1	0	8	7	6	0	7	4
7	6		4		8	7		1	9				7	8
2	9		1		5	5		6	7	5		9	8	1
8	4				7	8		4	5	2		2	2	9
6	4		5		4	9		6	0	7		2	7	8
7	9		4		7	7		2	0	4		1	5	6
5	0	9	1	4	2	7	6	8	7	1	9	4	6	4
6	4	5	8	7	1	2	2	9	9	0	7	1	5	7
	5	6	2				9				7			
	7	6	9		5	6	2		7	6	9	8		4
	4	1	7			8	7			2	1	5		4
	9	8	5		2	4	1		6	5	7	9		0
			6				1		4	5	9	2		7
5	6	5	9	8	1	2	0	4	6	5	8	1	9	7
6	6	9	1	8	2	4	2	2	0	9	8	1	7	5

Clubhouse Lingo (page 13)

Home plate, battery, can of corn, ace, backstop, triple crown

Word Columns (page 13)

"Ability is the art of getting credit for all the home runs somebody else hits."

Code-doku (page 14)

GROVE, MAYS

M	R	O	Y	S	G	V	A	E
G	S	A	V	E	O	M	Y	R
E	Y	V	R	A	M	O	G	S
R	M	Y	G	V	S	E	O	A
V	O	S	E	M	A	G	R	Y
A	E	G	O	R	Y	S	M	V
Y	V	M	A	O	E	R	S	G
S	G	E	M	Y	R	A	V	O
O	A	R	S	G	V	Y	E	M

Play Ball! (page 14)

1. art/tar; 2. has/ash; 3. arm/mar; 4. owl/low; 5. won/now; 6. opt/top

Baseball Teams Letterbox (page 15)

1	2	3	4	5	6	7	8	9	10	11	12	13
A	N	G	E	L	S	Y	K	U	R	P	B	D
14	15	16	17	18	19	20	21	22	23	24	25	26
M	X	I	W	J	H	C	V	T	O	**F**	**Q**	**Z**

Word Search (page 16)

Leftover letters: "I've found that you don't need to wear a necktie if you can hit."

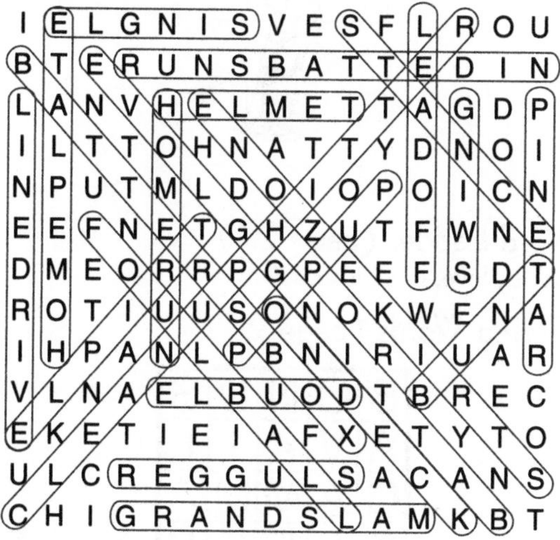

Chalk Talk (page 17)

Split-finger fastball, squeeze play, strikeout the side, top half of the inning, uppercut, ahead in the count

Shifter (page 17)

Swing Batter! (page 18)

Word Ladder (page 19)

BASE, bass, bats, hats, HITS

Rhyme Time (page 19)

1. low throw; 2. Stan's fans; 3. swing ring; 4. loyal Royal; 5. loud crowd; 6. stat chat; 7. power hour

Ballpark Flicks (pages 20-21)

Sequence (page 22)

A. Rangers, Angels, Mariners, Athletics

All the teams in the American League West.

Answers

Codeword (page 22)

K	O	N	E	R	K	O			V	E	R	B
I		O		E		W		A		N		U
N	I	X		J	E	N	K	S		D	Y	E
G		I		E				K		O		H
S	N	O	W	C	A	P		S	E	W	E	R
		U		T		R						L
A	B	S		S	K	I	E	R		B	E	E
Q						M		A		E		
U	N	R	I	G		P	U	M	I	C	E	D
I		A		A				I		K		A
F	A	T		F	E	W	E	R		H	E	N
E		I		F		O		E		A		K
R	I	O	S			E	N	Z	Y	M	E	S

K	U	Y	P	G	E	H	A	O	S	L	Z	N
M	Q	J	C	T	B	V	F	D	W	R	X	I

Rhyme Time (page 23)

1. squeeze please; 2. strike spike; 3. Sandy's dandies; 4. sweeter heater; 5. swing king; 6. scout bout; 7. one run

Wacky Wordy (page 23)

Who's on First?

Play Ball (page 24)

1. catch, 2. bunt, 3. base, 4. single, 5. pitch, 6. umpire, 7. triple, 8. shortstop, 9. manager, 10. diamond

At Bat (page 25)

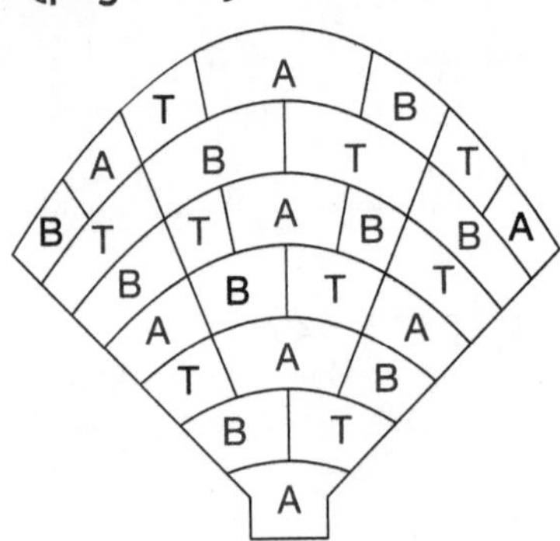

New Franchises? (page 25)

1. Cardinals; 2. Mariners

Picture This (page 26)

Word Ladder (page 27)

SAVE, lave, love, lose, LOSS

Fitting Words (page 27)

Word Jigsaw (page 28)

Network (page 28)

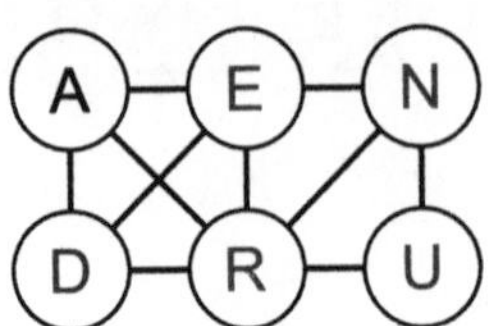

At the Plate (page 29)

Leftover letters: pinch hitter, ball, shortstop

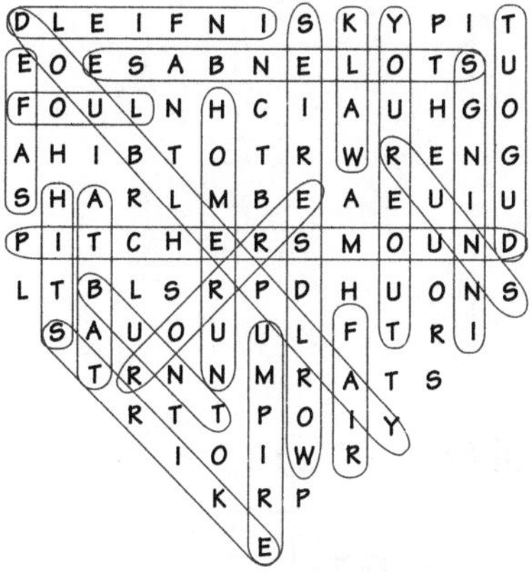

It's Outta Here! (page 30)

Wacky Wordy (page 30)

Doubleheader

Word Columns (page 31)

"Finding good players is easy. Getting them to play as a team is another story."

Baseball Superstitions (page 31)

Did you know that Ty Cobb brought a black bat to every game during the 1907 season, but never used it once?

Play Ball! (pages 32–33)

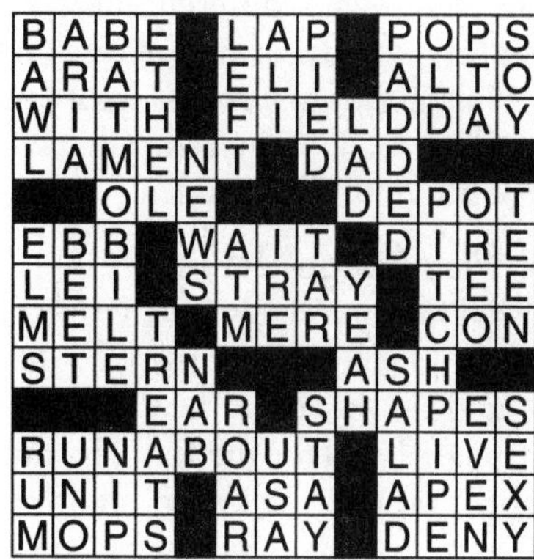

Baseball Tamagram (page 34)

Ace pitcher (catcher pie)

Elevator Words (page 35)

1. BALL four; 2. four score; 3. scoreboard; 4. board game; 5. game highlights; 6. highlights REEL

Grid Fill (page 35)

Mix n' Match (page 36)

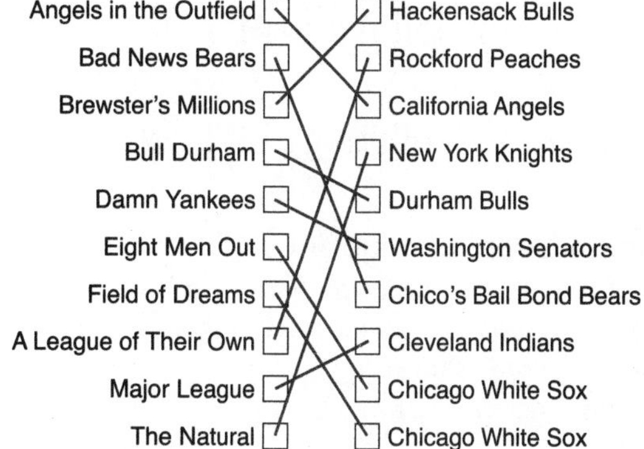

Answers

Screwball (page 37)

1. shoes are different; 2. different bushes in background; 3. mountains instead of clouds; 4. number missing from jersey; 5. more motion lines around baseball; 6. cap removed; 7. ball in different position; 8. watch added.

Years of Play (page 38)

Harry played for the Angels for 3 years. Since he played for the Orioles longer than for the Mariners, and he played for the Orioles a year longer than he played for the Rays, he must have played for the Orioles for 5 years and therefore for the Rays for 4 years. Since he played for the Mariners a year longer than for the Yankees, he must have played for the Mariners for 2 years and for the Yankees for 1 year.

Fastball (page 39)

There are 70 baseballs.

Double Jumble (page 40)

S ABSENCE S

U WETNESS E

B UPGRADE R

W STIMULI I

A YELLOWS E

Y BARRIER S

Team Search (page 41)

Leftover letters: "A team is where a boy can prove his courage on his own. A gang is where a coward goes to hide."

Bonus answer: Diamondbacks

```
A T E A M S S I S S W H E B R
E S A B B T S C R A N G E R S
O E S Y R N S E I K C O R E N
C E A R I A G Y N T N P R W A
O K V L E I V A A E E H I E I
S N R C T G T E O J U L P R D
R A S A S I D S S T E M H S N
M Y E A O L G O N E O U I T I
N S T N H C A R D I N A L S A
I E A G A S O Y W N W S L B A
G L R E D S O X O S E T I H W
S O I L A N T M A R I N E R S
G I P S I S W R D A E H S E B
R R E A C O W A O Y A D R D U
G O O E S T P O H S I D S E C
```

Grid Fill (page 42)

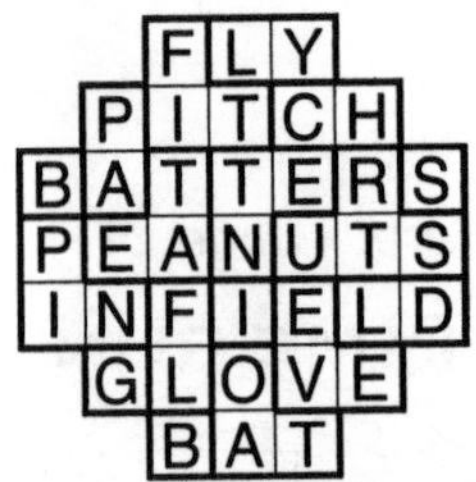

Take Me Out to the Ball Game (page 42)

9648	BASE
9622	BALL
+ 16784	GAMES
36054	YANKS

A=6, B=9, E=8, G=1, K=5, L=2, M=7, N=0, S=4, Y=3

Word Columns (page 43)

"Trying to sneak a pitch past Hank Aaron is like trying to sneak a sunrise past a rooster."

Hall of Fame Nicknames (page 43)

1. Wade Boggs; 2. Carl Hubbell; 3. Casey Stengel; 4. Duke Snider

The Right Stuff (page 44)

1. towel added to pack; 2. bucket handle flipped; 3. bag zipped; 4. bat missing; 5. water bottle added to bag; 6. helmet appeared on bench; 7. no stripes on jersey; 8. baseball now in mitt; 9. shoes flipped; 10. no fence in background

Name Calling (page 45)

"A hot dog at the ballgame beats roast beef at the Ritz."

Shifter (page 45)

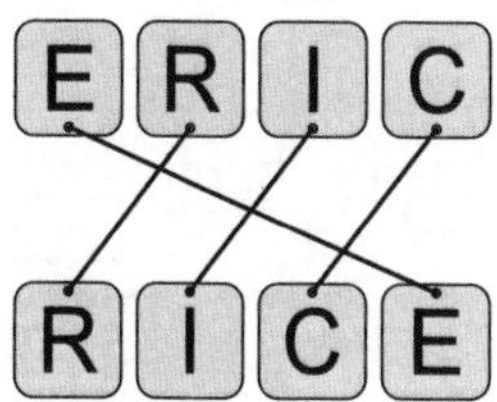

Baseball Terminology Letterbox (page 46)

1	2	3	4	5	6	7	8	9	10	11	12	13
H	O	M	E	R	U	N	Z	X	J	Y	L	V
14	15	16	17	18	19	20	21	22	23	24	25	26
K	W	S	F	C	P	B	D	G	I	T	A	**Q**

Going . . . Going . . . Gone! (page 47)

1. "Bye bye baby!"; 2. "Forget it!"; 3. " Get out the rye bread and mustard grandma, cause it's grand salami time!"; 4. "Goodbye baseball!"; 5. "Holy cow!"; 6. "It could be, it might be . . . it is! A home run!"; 7. "Kiss it goodbye!"; 8. "That ball is going and it ain't coming back!"; 9. "They usually show movies on a flight like that."; 10. "Back, back, back, back . . . Gone!"

Close Call (page 48)

1. home plate is a star; 2. catcher's hand is disconnected; 3. balloon in the dust; 4. catcher wearing a football helmet; 5. jersey says "Rodgers"; 6. baseline going through runner; 7. umpire is on roller skates; 8. umpire has one short pant leg

Lineup Card (page 49)

1. Leo Durocher; 2. Pee Wee Reese; 3. Duke Snider; 4. Jackie Robinson; 5. Don Drysdale; 6. Sandy Koufax; 7. Tommy Lasorda; 8. Don Sutton; 9. Gil Hodges; 10. Steve Garvey
Team: Dodgers

Fitting Words (page 50)

Yer Out! (page 51)

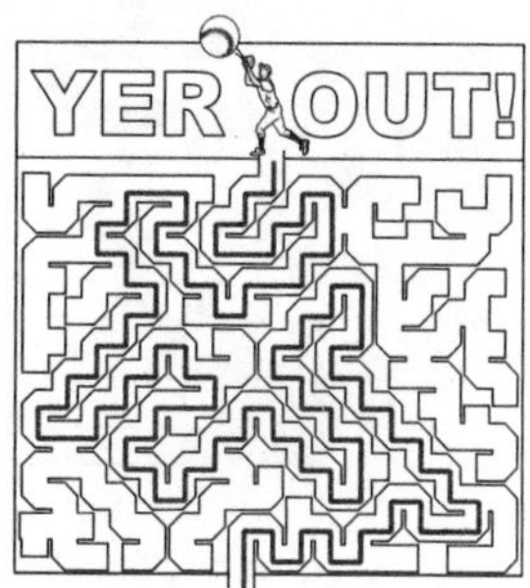

Full Count (page 52)

There are 95 instances of BASEBALL in the grid.

Codeword (page 53)

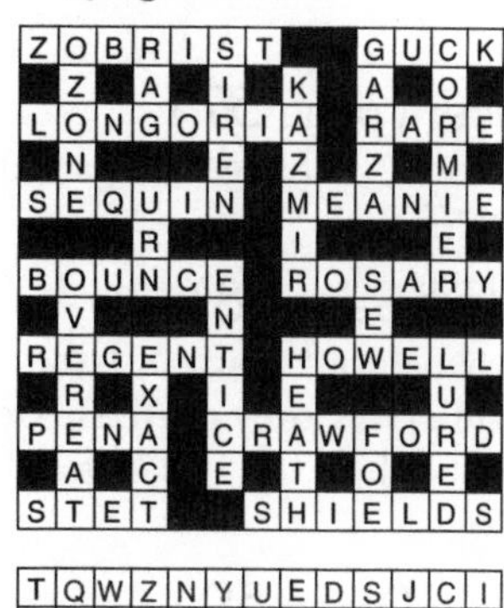

T	Q	W	Z	N	Y	U	E	D	S	J	C	I
H	L	X	G	R	A	F	K	B	M	P	O	V

Chalk Talk (page 54)

Behind in the count, blown save, cleanup hitter, cut fastball, ducks on the pond, check the runner

How Much? (page 54)

Jacques, the catcher, made $8 million.
Lefty, the pitcher, made $10 million.
Peydey, the first baseman, made $12 million.
LeBucks, the shortstop, made $14 million.

Answers

Rhyme Time (page 55)

1. thin Twin; 2. hipper skipper; 3. bitter hitter; 4. Cal's pals; 5. plump ump; 6. zone prone; 7. slow throw; 8. high fly; 9. newer Brewer; 10. Joe's blows

Pic-a-Pix (page 56)

Word Jigsaw (page 57)

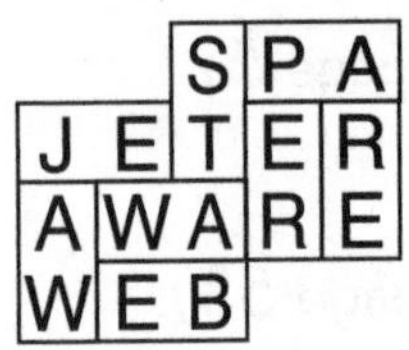

Word Ladder (page 57)

BATTER, banter, barter, garter, garner, gurner, BURNER

Picture This (page 58)

Yogi (Lawrence Berra), Catfish (James Hunter), Big Mac (Willie McCovey or Mark McGwire), The Iron Horse (Lou Gehrig), Satchel (Leroy Paige)

Rhyme Time (page 59)

1. Yankee hanky; 2. Greg's legs; 3. rookie's cookies; 4. tall wall; 5. switch pitch; 6. dark park; 7. fatter batter; 8. spook Duke

Swing Batter! (page 60)

Baseball Able Labs (page 61)

1. team/tame; 2. eats/seat; 3. felt/left; 4. tarp/part; 5. lope/pole; 6. Lots/lost

Word Ladder (page 61)

Answers may vary.

BALL, fall, fail, foil, foul, FOUR

Say It Ain't So! (page 62)

Leftover letters: Although he refused to join in the fix, third baseman Buck Weaver was banned with the others for not reporting it.

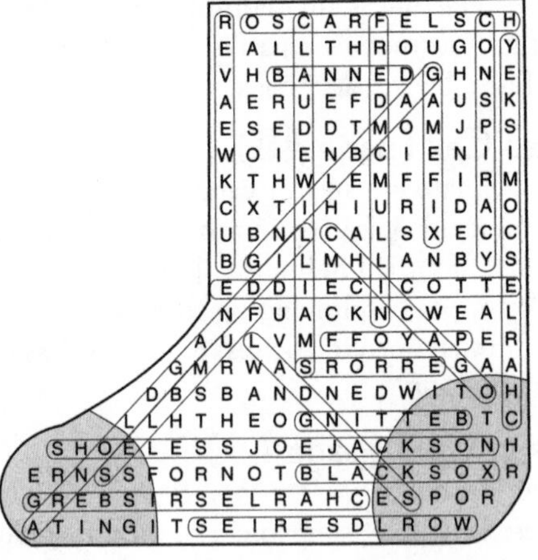

He's the Man(ager) (page 63)

Philadelphia A's (now the Oakland Athletics) manager Connie Mack has 3,731 career victories, more than any other manager in history.

Shifter (page 63)

Curveball (page 64)

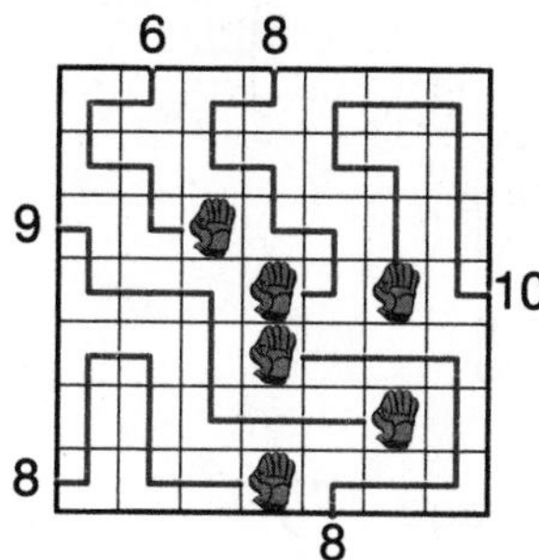

Network (page 65)

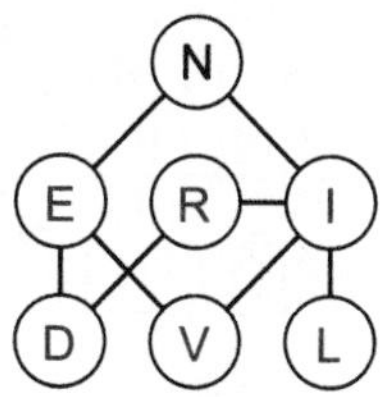

Word Ladder (page 65)

Answers may vary.
RAG, brag, brat, beat, bent, BUNT

Pitcher Perfect (page 66)

Grid Fill (page 67)

Word Jigsaw (page 67)

Batter Up! (page 68)

Silhouette 2 is an exact match.

Rhyme Time (page 69)

1. tame game/lame game; 2. Twins grins; 3. home run won; 4. stadium bum; 5. wider slider; 6. mask task; 7. postgame claim; 8. can't play today; 9. shortstop flop; 10. stolen base race; 11. trade rumor humor

What's the Score? (page 70)

Scoreboards 2 and 5 are identical.

Word Columns (page 71)

"Now there's three things you can do in a baseball game: You can win or you can lose or it can rain."

Smart Trams (page 71)

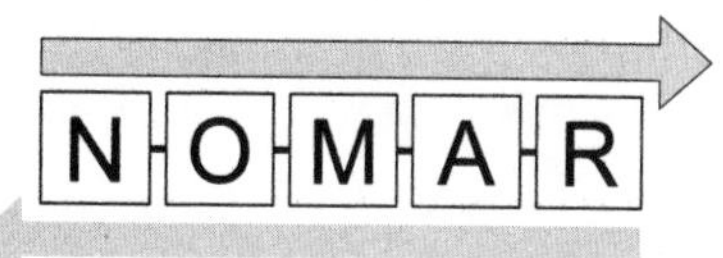

Answers

Chalk Talk (page 72)

Double-play depth, hanging curveball, lineup, bottom half of the inning, seventh-inning stretch, drag bunt

Grid Fill (page 73)

Double Jumble (page 74)

B LIFTOFF F

A BANDEAU O

L LANGUOR U

L AVOCADO R

Take Me Out to the Ball Game (page 75)

1. d) Lawrence; 2. c) Jay; 3. d) Johnny; 4. c) George; 5. d) Vincent; 6. a) Harold; 7. b) George; 8. c) Charles; 9. b) James; 10. d) Edwin

Word Jigsaw (page 76)

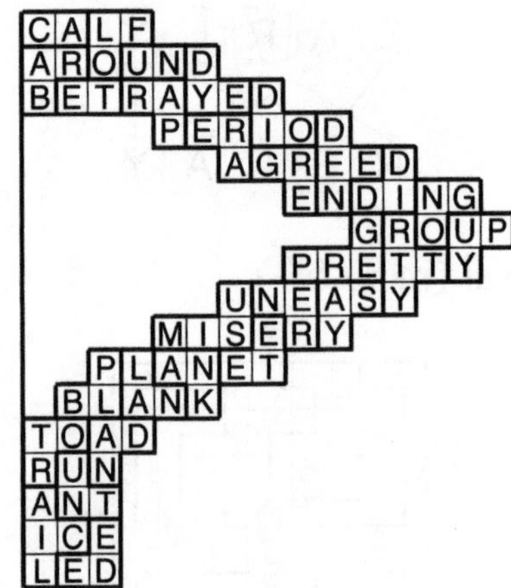

Grid Fill (page 77)

Network (page 77)

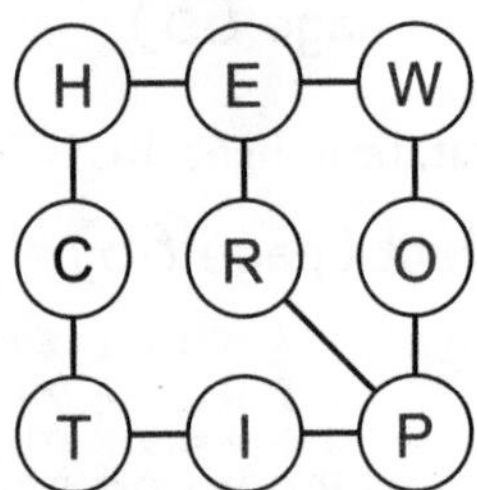

Name Calling (page 78)

Never make the final out at third.

Double Jumble (page 78)

L ETHICAL L

I TAPIOCA E

T LEGIBLE A

T LADYBUG G

L IMPULSE U

E TABLEAU E

Codeword (page 79)

A	K	C	D	U	O	J	X	G	W	F	E	T
R	N	B	S	P	M	I	Y	V	Z	L	H	Q

Pic-a-Pix (page 80)

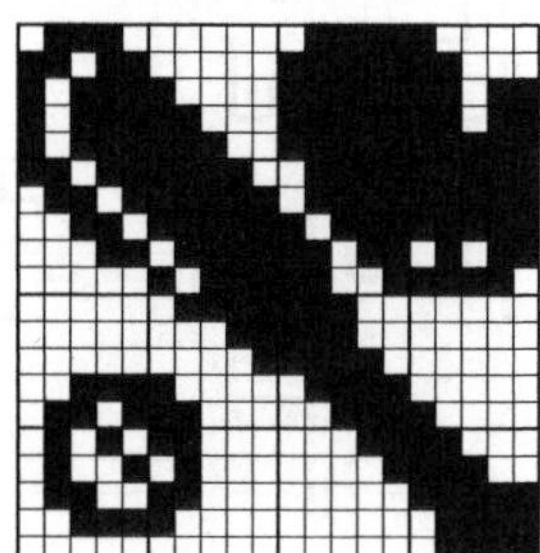

Baseball Homes Letterbox (page 81)

1	2	3	4	5	6	7	8	9	10	11	12	13
S	A	N	D	I	E	G	O	X	K	U	B	P
14	15	16	17	18	19	20	21	22	23	24	25	26
R	C	Z	M	W	T	H	F	V	L	Y	**J**	**Q**

Missing Connections (page 82)

Fitting Words (page 83)

K	E	N	Y	A
I	D	I	O	M
S	I	N	G	E
S	T	E	I	N

Word Jigsaw (page 83)

Picture This (page 84)

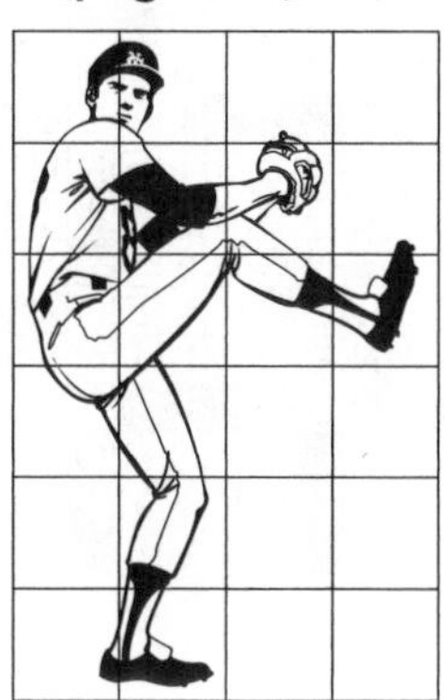

Answers

Rhyme Time (page 85)

1. delay play; 2. chilly Phillie; 3. permits hits; 4. right plight; 5. proud crowd; 6. farm arm; 7. worse curse; 8. mound bound; 9. career gear; 10. hot shot; 11. Met vet

RBI Players (page 86)

Dan had an RBI total of 44. Sam Waverly didn't have an RBI total of 40, and since his RBI wasn't in the 30s, by elimination Sam's RBI total was 42. Therefore, Mr. Short's RBI total must be 40, Jack's must be 38, and Mr. Templeton's must be 36. Also, Clark's last name is Templeton and Jack's last name is Emerald. Therefore, by elimination, Mr. Short's first name must be Mike, and Dan's last name must be Case.

Codeword (page 87)

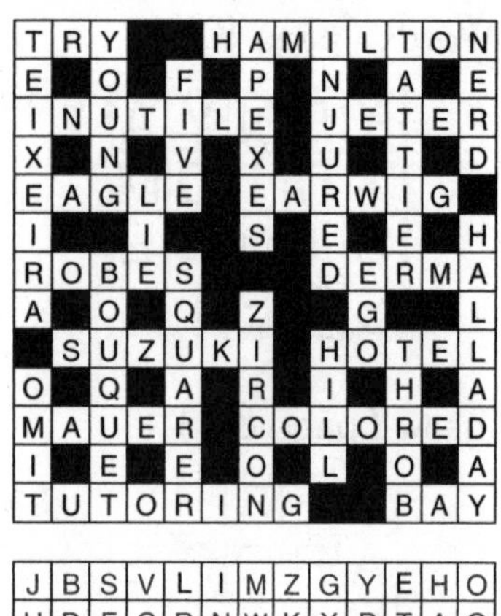

Ball Games (pages 88–89)

Code-doku (page 89)

F	U	I	S	N	Y	K	O	G
S	G	O	K	F	U	N	Y	I
Y	N	K	O	G	I	U	S	F
I	F	S	N	U	O	G	K	Y
G	O	Y	I	K	F	S	N	U
U	K	N	Y	S	G	F	I	O
O	S	U	G	Y	K	I	F	N
K	Y	F	U	I	N	O	G	S
N	I	G	F	O	S	Y	U	K

FISK, YOUNG

Double Jumble (page 90)

C UNEQUAL D

L LUMBAGO O

U HAYWIRE U

T CORNCOB B

C TABLOID L

H CHATEAU E

Yer Out! (page 91)

Diamond Detective (page 92)

The missing word is DAIRY. The second letters of each word, reading down, would then spell ROYALS. The fourth letters of each word, reading down, would spell PADRES.

Get Yer Peanuts! (page 93)

Silhouette number 5 matches the illustration.

It's a Spiritual Thing (page 93)

"I've tried 'em all, I really have, and the only church that truly feeds the soul, day in, day out, is the Church of Baseball."

—Annie Savoy in "Bull Durham"

Grid Fill (page 94)

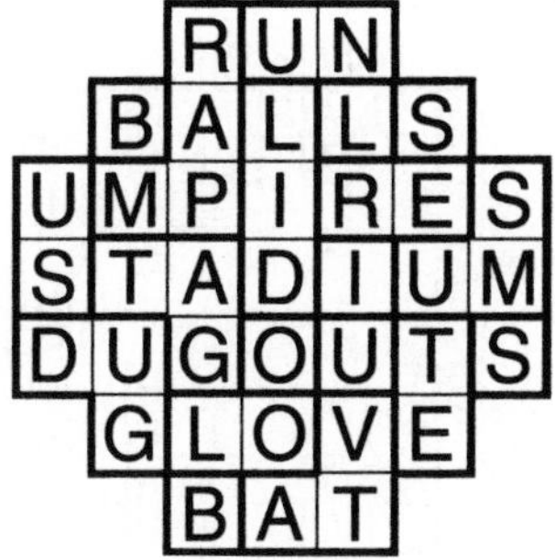

Word Columns (page 94)

"No baseball pitcher would be worth a darn without a catcher who could handle the hot fastball."

Baseball and the White House (Part II) (page 96)

1. False; 2. Harry S. Truman; 3. pitcher; 4. Clinton administration; 5. True

Rhyme Time (page 96)

1. Twin win; 2. vine shrine; 3. slow pro; 4. last blast; 5. relieve Steve; 6. hill skill; 7. A's craze

It's Outta Here! (page 97)

Baseball Tamagram (page 98)

Scalable (ball case)

Fitting Words (page 98)

It's Like Déjà Vu . . . (Part II) (page 100)

Baseball diamond, Batter, Baseball cap, Mitt, Hot dog

Baseball Quirks (page 100)

"Say 'Dodgers' and people know you're talking about baseball. Say 'Braves' and they ask, 'What reservation?' Say 'Reds' and they think of communism. Say 'Padres' and they look around for a priest."

—Tommy Lasorda

Answers

Ted's Trophies (page 101)

1. laurel leaves; 2. same base; 3. triple posts; 4. MVP engraved; 5. a star on each; 6. all have a baseball player holding a bat; 7. 2010 engraved; 8. baseball in each

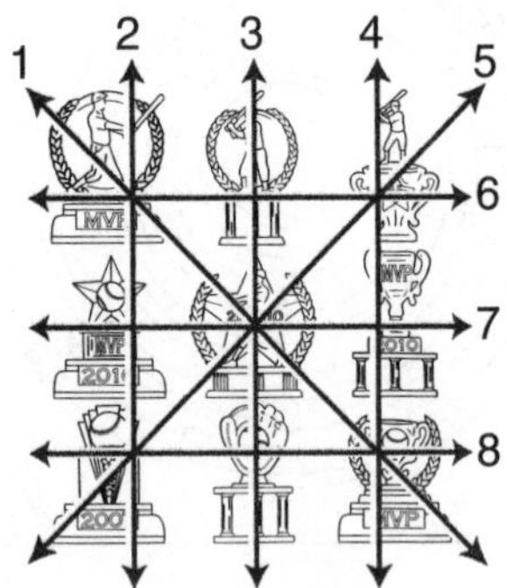

Word Ladder (page 101)

HOME, hone, honk, hunk, hung, rung, RUNS

MLB Records (pages 102–103)

Breaking the Baseball Color Line (page 103)

"The right of every American to first-class citizenship is the most important issue of our time."

Missing Connections (page 104)

Network (page 105)

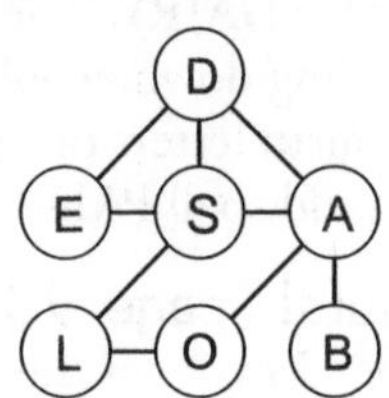

Lineup Card (page 105)

1. Yogi Berra; 2. Lou Gehrig; 3. Derek Jeter; 4. Babe Ruth; 5. Joe DiMaggio; 6. Mickey Mantle; 7. Thurman Munson

Team: Yankees

Word Jigsaw (page 106)

Double Jumble (page 107)

R OREGANO S

O ILLNESS E

O REGALIA A

K KNUCKLE S

I ECHELON O

E OBVIOUS N

Word Ladder (page 108)

SPIT, slit, slid, said, sail, bail, BALL

Hidden Ball Trick (page 108)

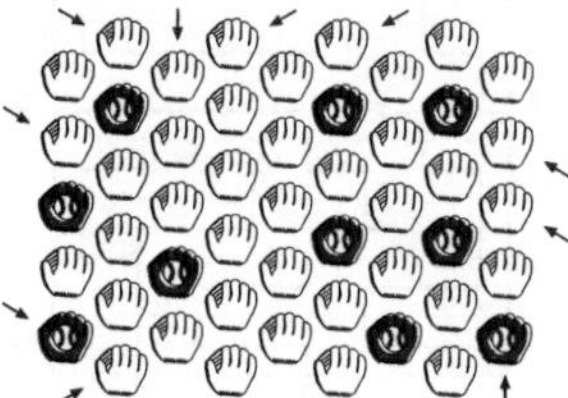

Codeword (page 109)

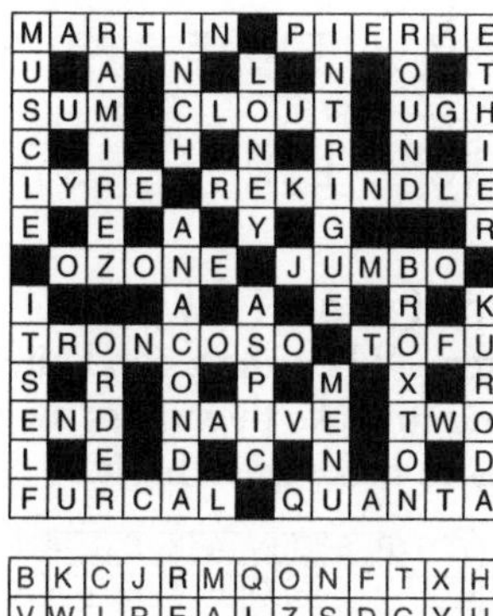

Idioms from the Diamond (pages 110-111)

Bang-Bang Play (page 112)

Boxes 2 and 5 are exactly alike.

Left, Right, and Center (page 113)

Leftover letters: "Correct thinkers think that 'baseball trivia' is an oxymoron: Nothing about baseball is trivial."

Original player: Ashburn

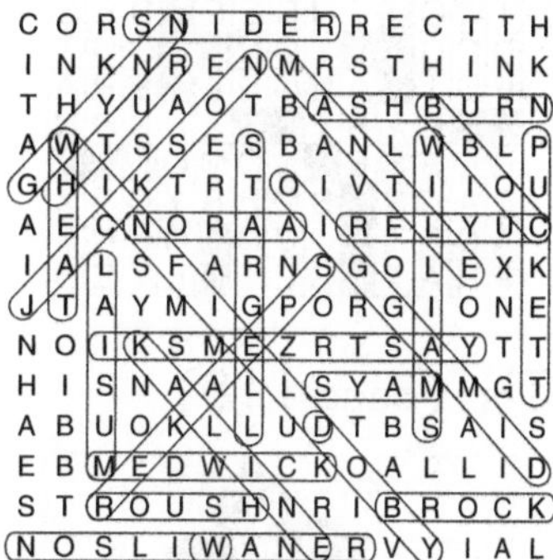

Word Jigsaw (page 114)

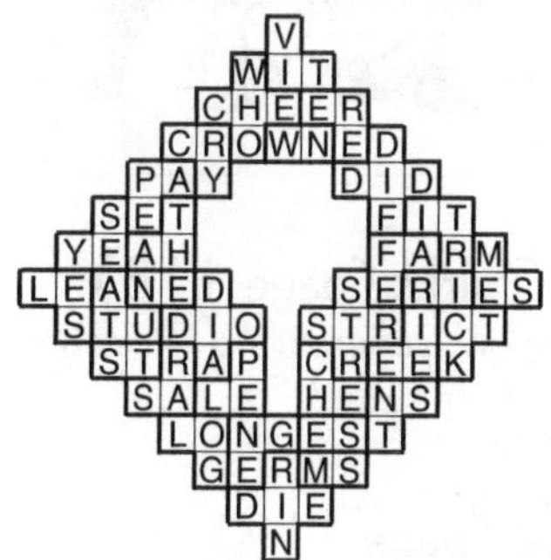

Double Jumble (page 115)

B TRAFFIC C

A ARCHAIC O

T GRANOLA A

T ISTHMUS C

I BRAVADO H

N NOMINEE E

G TRIUMPH S

Answers

The Name Game (pages 116–117)

Picture This (page 118)

Baseball Quirks (page 118)

"I have only one superstition—touch all the bases when I hit a home run."

—Babe Ruth

Codeword (page 119)

K	S	Y	X	F	H	C	L	P	D	O	B	J
R	W	U	V	M	Z	E	T	N	A	Q	I	G

Curveball (page 120)

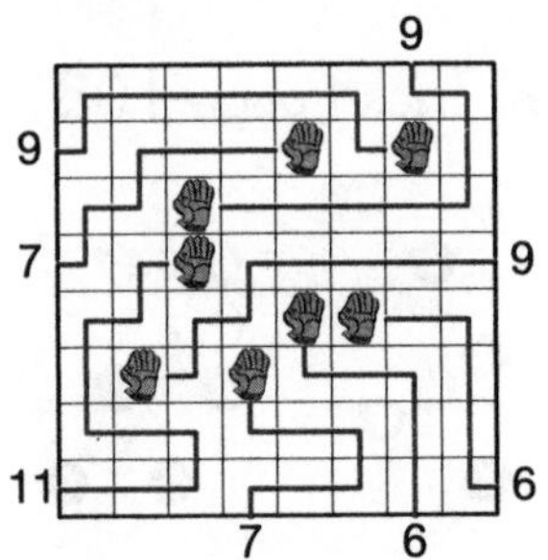

Shifter (page 120)

Hurler Hunt (page 121)

Leftover letters: "I became a good pitcher when I stopped trying to make them miss the ball and started trying to make them hit it."

```
I B Y E R E D N A X E L A C A
M S E A V E R O R K E I N E A
G G L O O N O S B I G D P I T
R C S H E R F W L R W O H E N
O I R S T O F E L L E R M P P
V E E M W I L H E L M T D E T
E R K C N Y I T D Y A B N N Z
L J C G G T O A D M R A K U E
A T E I H E M M A O I R M I H
D R N N O M E L W S C S E C U
S T A N K H E N Y B H A A P B
Y Y E I H I L L N A A R N A B
R D D T S A N T N A L R Y L E
D T E Y D T P S U T T O N M L
R Y I J O H N S O N U N G E L
T O M A B U N N I N G K E R T
H E M H I T I T G N I F F U R
```

Have a Ball (page 122)

1. ball boy; 2. ball club; 3. ball girl; 4. dead ball; 5. fork ball; 6. fly ball; 7. money ball; 8. screwball

Shifter (page 122)

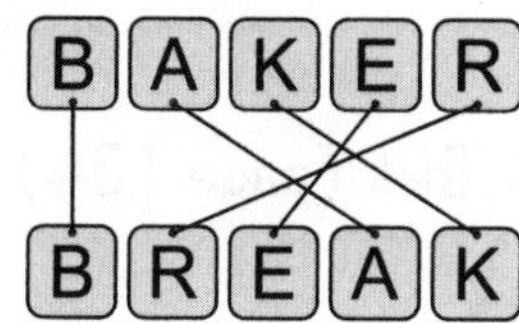

Lineup Card (page 123)

1. George Brett; 2. Fred Patek; 3. Hal McRae; 4. Frank White; 5. Dan Quisenberry; 6. Bo Jackson; 7. Willie Wilson; 8. Amos Otis
Team: Royals

Network (page 123)

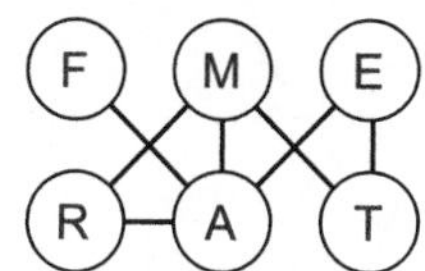

Pinstripe Club (pages 124–125)

Leftover letters: "Managing is getting paid for home runs someone else hits."

M	A	N	A	G	E	T	T	I	T	T	E	P	G	I
N	G	I	S	O	N	O	S	N	U	M	A	R	I	S
R	U	T	H	M	G	J	A	C	K	S	O	N	E	S
I	E	T	T	E	Y	L	G	N	I	T	T	A	M	I
C	G	N	G	Z	H	S	S	I	L	B	M	A	H	C
H	A	P	M	R	E	H	S	I	W	S	I	H	M	A
A	S	B	A	I	N	U	D	F	O	L	R	S	H	A
R	S	O	R	O	D	M	G	W	L	O	P	E	Z	R
D	O	T	T	E	E	T	E	I	X	E	I	R	A	R
S	G	U	I	D	R	Y	W	N	R	E	R	T	E	E
O	E	Z	N	U	S	A	N	F	E	D	F	Y	S	B
N	H	Z	S	O	O	M	E	I	T	N	O	M	A	D
O	R	I	M	A	N	T	L	E	E	B	R	R	N	E
E	I	R	I	V	E	R	A	L	J	L	D	S	E	H
I	G	T	Y	E	K	C	I	D	R	A	W	O	H	S

Code-doku (page 125)

BANKS, RUTH

A	U	H	S	N	R	K	T	B
S	B	T	K	A	U	N	R	H
R	N	K	T	B	H	U	S	A
H	A	S	N	U	T	B	K	R
B	T	R	H	K	A	S	N	U
U	K	N	R	S	B	A	H	T
T	S	U	B	R	K	H	A	N
K	R	A	U	H	N	T	B	S
N	H	B	A	T	S	R	U	K

Rhyme Time (page 126)

1. immense fence; 2. locker stocker; 3. slender vendor; 4. swift shift; 5. missed assist; 6. Prince's blintzes; 7. spaces bases; 8. playoff payoff; 9. niche pitch; 10. safe waif; 11. Yogi's hoagies; 12. austere cheer; 13. more score; 14. slider provider; 15. winning inning

Pic-a-Pix (page 127)

Strikeout Kings (pages 128–129)

Leftover letters: "Nolan Ryan is the only guy who could put fear in me. Not because he could get me out but because he could kill me."

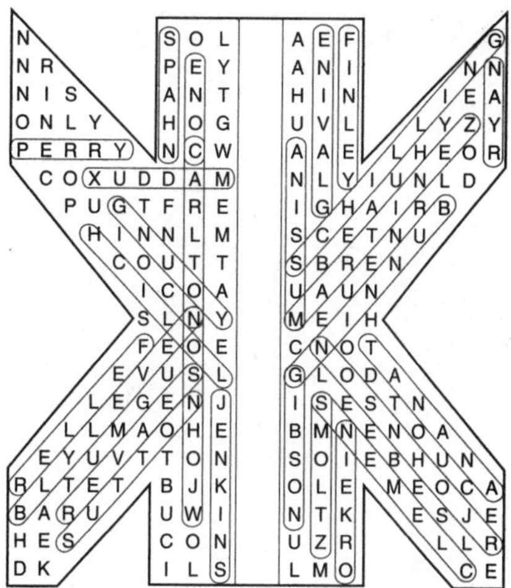

Word Ladder (page 129)

Answers may vary.
FOUL, fool, foot, loot, loft, lift, life/lint, LINE

Baseball Tamagram (page 130)

Botanic (bat icon)

Answers

Network (page 130)

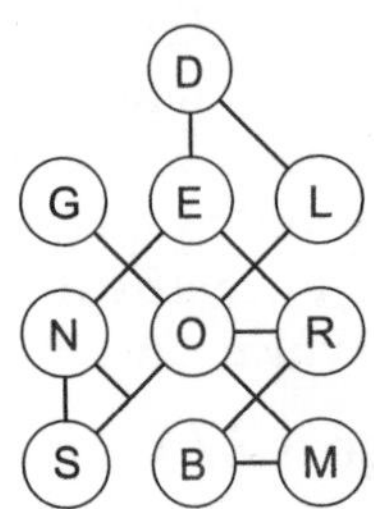

Ballpark Lingo (page 131)

1. around the horn; 2. caught looking; 3. meatball; 4. Texas leaguer

Utility Man (page 131)

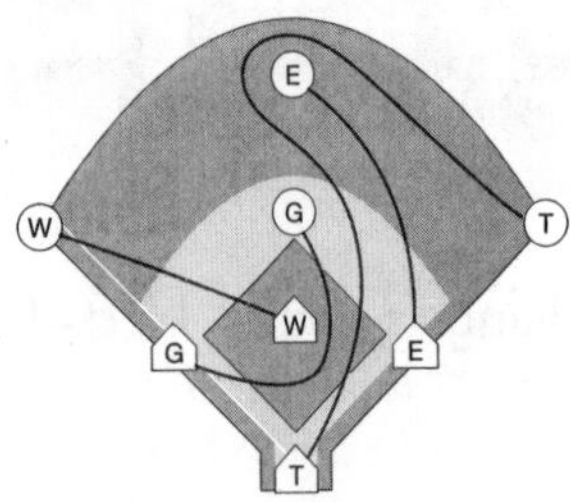

Sluggers (pages 132–133)

Leftover letters: "Losing feels worse than winning feels good."

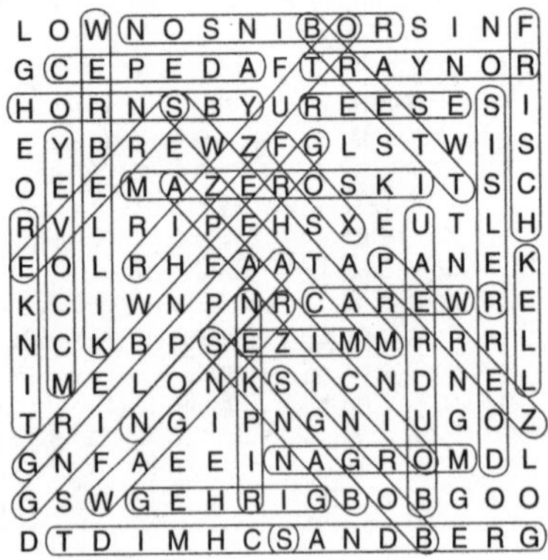

Word Columns (page 133)

You know why it's always cool at San Francisco baseball games? It's all those Giant fans.

Anagram Heroes (page 134)

1. Mickey Mantle; 2. Derek Jeter; 3. Joe Montana is not a Yankees great. 4. Whitey Ford

Hidden Ball Trick (page 134)

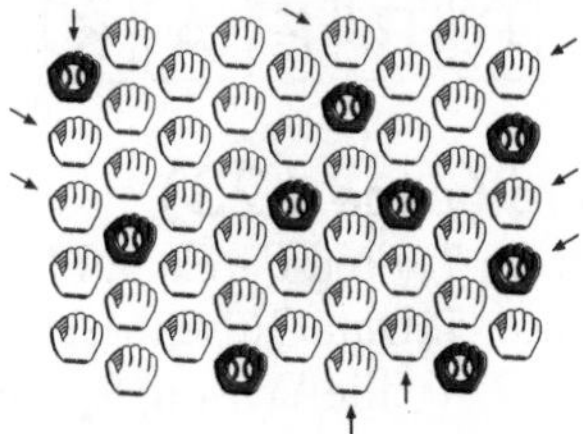

Mix n' Match (page 135)

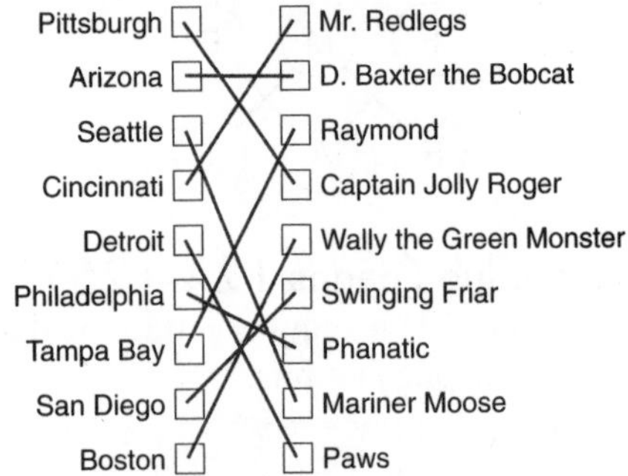

Unforgettable Teams? (Part II) (page 136)

Braves, Red Sox, Reds, Dodgers, Phillies, Astros, Mets

Codeword (page 136)

B	G	U	C	P	H	T	Z	L	W	I	D	J
X	F	O	R	M	A	N	K	Y	Q	S	V	E

Yer Out! (page 137)

Triple Crown (pages 138–139)

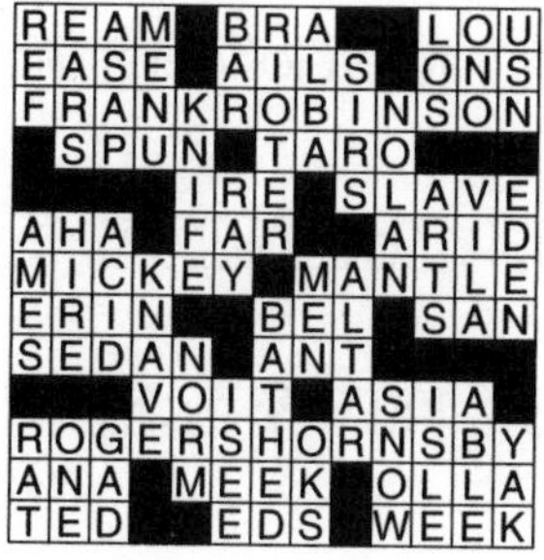

You Heard It Here First (page 140)

"I'd always heard it couldn't be done, but sometimes it don't always work."

—Hall of Fame Manager Casey Stengel

Missing Connections (page 140)

Fireballer (page 141)

There are 10 baseballs.

Play Ball! (page 141)

1. worth/throw; 2. rated/trade; 3. idles/slide; 4. steal/least; 5. pleat/plate

It's Outta Here! (page 142)

Lineup Card (page 143)

1. Lou Brock; 2. Dizzy Dean; 3. Bob Gibson; 4. Stan Musial; 5. Enos Slaughter; 6. Ozzie Smith; 7. Rogers Hornsby; 8. Bruce Sutter

Team: Cardinals

Network (page 143)

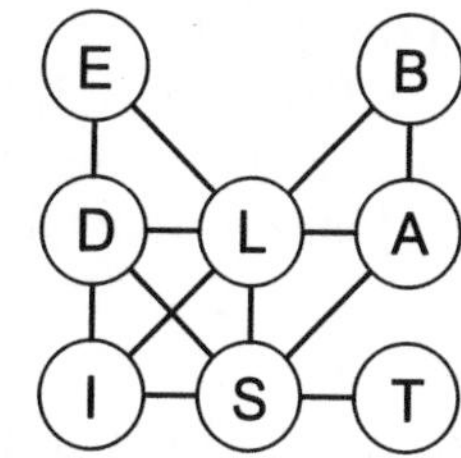

Picture This (page 144)

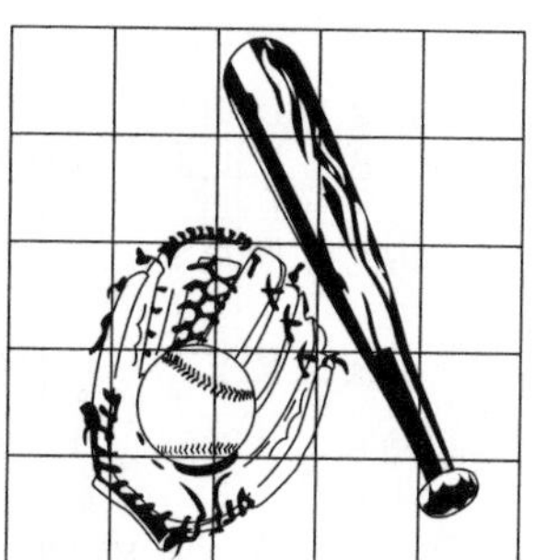

Answers

Rhyme Time (page 145)

1. head red; 2. chief thief; 3. sham slam; 4. brief relief; 5. Greinke's hankies; 6. Ranger danger; 7. slide guide; 8. team scheme; 9. Rocket's pockets; 10. hit fit; 11. base chase; 12; stitch glitch; 13. walk talk; 14. star's scars; 15. error terror; 16. double trouble

Working Title (page 146)

"Angels in the Outfield," "Field of Dreams," "Major League," "Bull Durham," "Bang the Drum Slowly"

Point Counterpoint (page 146)

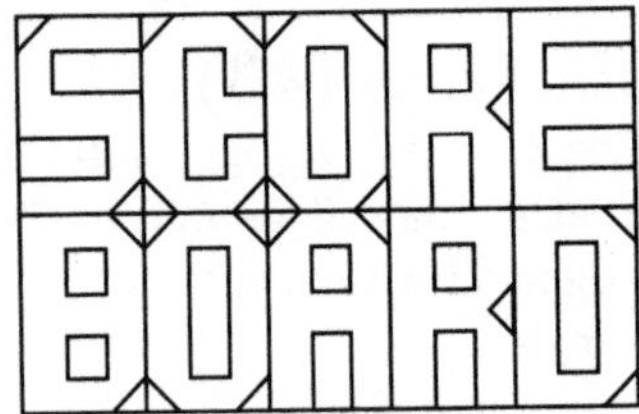

Lineup Card (page 147)

1. Dale Murphy; 2. Phil Niekro; 3. Hank Aaron; 4. Warren Spahn; 5. Eddie Mathews; 6. Andruw Jones; 7. Chipper Jones; 8. Tom Glavine; 9. Greg Maddux

Team: Braves

Word Search (pages 148–149)

Leftover letters: "I was such a dangerous hitter I even got intentional walks during batting practice."

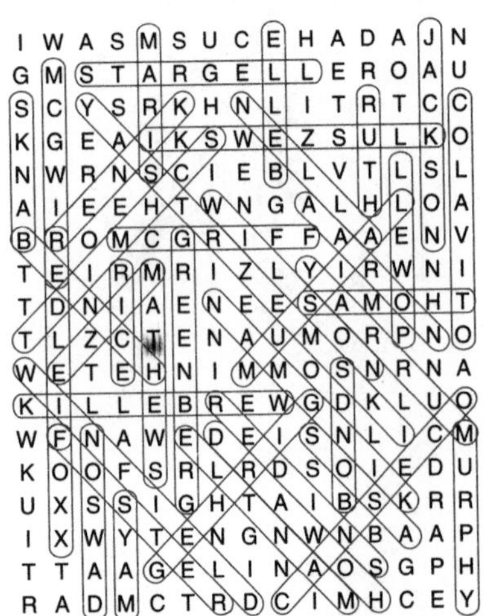

Play Ball! (page 149)

1. source/course; 2. Expect/except; 3. rescue/secure; 4. center/recent; 5. umpire/impure; 6. replay/player

Double Jumble (page 150)

B LAWLESS D

A AVOCADO I

S EJECTED A

E BELOVED M

B AMMONIA O

A BLOSSOM N

L LIAISON D

L STIMULI S

Swing Batter! (page 151)

Hidden Ball Trick (page 152)

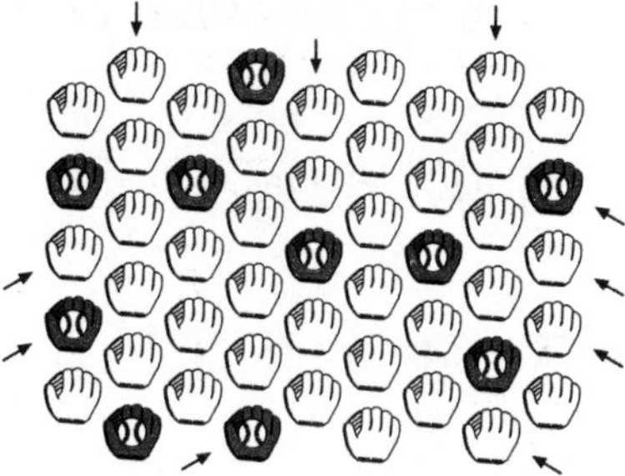

Word Ladder (page 152)

Answers may vary.

PLAY, pray, bray, brat, beat, belt, bell, BALL

Missing Connections (page 153)

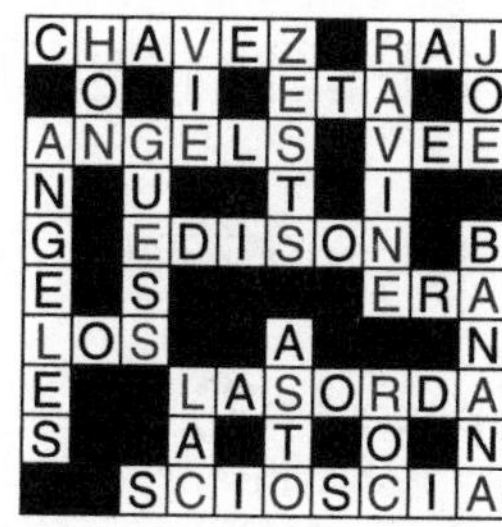

Utility Man (page 153)

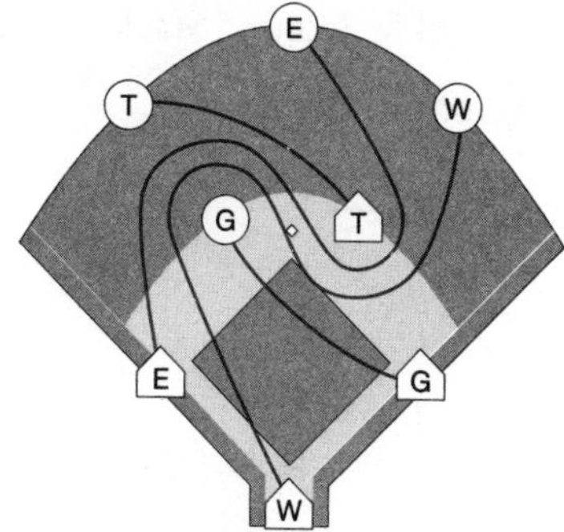

Chalk Talk (page 154)

falcon + skirt = Carlton Fisk;
rope + tees = Pete Rose;
ark + pencil = Cal Ripken;
rook + club = Lou Brock;
atom + serve = Tom Seaver

Mix n' Match (page 154)

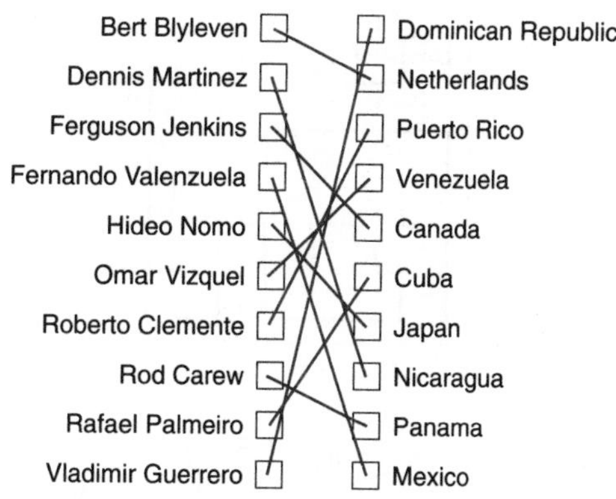

Double Jumble (page 155)

S TWELFTH P

T INSPECT I

A SATIRIC T

R ANXIOUS C

T GLIMPSE H

I NONSTOP E

N TRAITOR R

G RAVIOLI S

Lineup Card (page 156)

1. Casey Stengel; 2. Gil Hodges; 3. Tom Seaver;
4. Rusty Staub; 5. Darryl Strawberry;
6. Dwight Gooden

Team: Mets

Answers

Curveball (page 156)

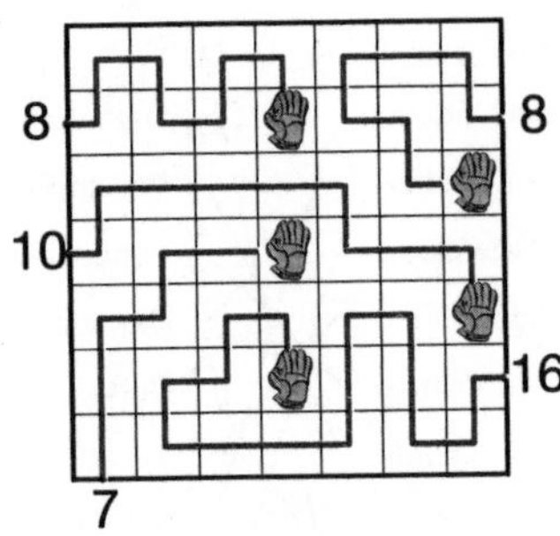

Double Jumble (page 161)

L FATUOUS B

E LENIENT A

A ABREAST T

D OFFICER T

O FORMULA E

F DISTURB R

F EARACHE S

Word Columns (page 157)

"Casey Stengel knew his baseball. He only made it look like he was fooling around. He knew every move that was ever invented and some that we haven't even caught on to yet."

Working Title (page 158)

"Damn Yankees," "A League of Their Own," "Bad News Bears," "Eight Men Out," "The Natural"

Lipstick on a Pig Dept. (page 158)

"Me carrying a briefcase is like a hot dog wearing earrings."

—Sparky Anderson

Baseball Basics (Part I) (page 159)

1. a (Only the catcher and first baseman are allowed, though not required, to use mitts); 2. his cap or his pocket; 3. squeeze; 4. b; 5. c (in a World Series game there are umpires at home plate, 1st base, 2nd base, 3rd base, left field, and right field)

Baseball Basics (Part II) (page 160)

1. false; 2. false; 3. true; 4. false; 5. false

Word Columns (page 160)

"The best possible thing in baseball is winning the World Series. The second best thing is losing the World Series."

Chalk Talk (page 162)

bib + bongos = Bob Gibson;
wallet + lei + girls = Willie Stargell;
fan + cork + list = Carlton Fisk;
wand + dive + file = Dave Winfield;
can + ice + monk = Connie Mack

Network (page 162)

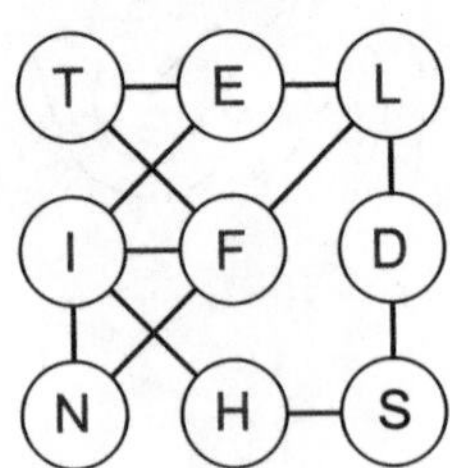

College Baseball by Alpha Sleuth™ (page 163)

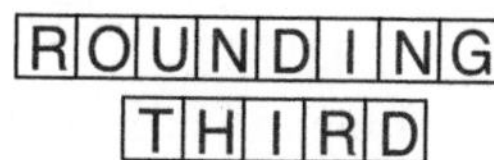

Home Games (pages 164–165)

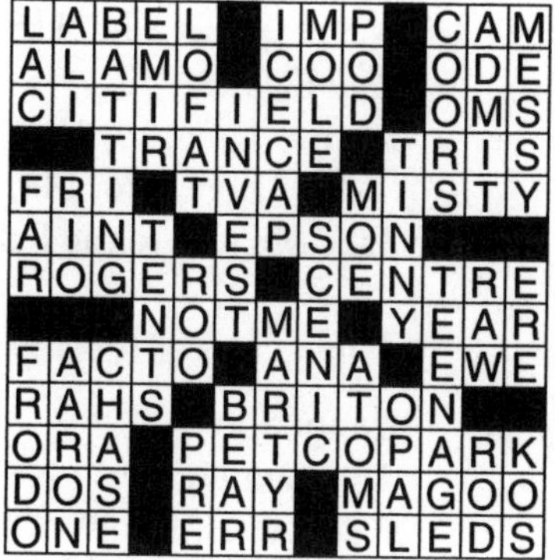

Picture This (page 166)

Word Ladder (page 166)

Answers may vary.

AWAY, awry, airy ,wiry, wire, tire, time, tame, GAME

Rhyme Time (page 167)

1. Sox Fox; 2. balk talk; 3. Padres stay; 4. Mays say heys; 5. foul poll toll; 6. base path math; 7. bona fide slide; 8. home runs begun; 9. scoreboard lord; 10. Mudville thrill; 11. Big Papi's happy; 12. draft pick trick; 13. autograph gaffe

Index

Logic

Mazes

Memory

Planning

Problem Solving

Spatial Reasoning

Spatial Visualization

Visual Logic

Visual Search

Word Searches